'I'm afraid that you have sealed your fate.'

Jade felt a shiver of apprehension trickle its way slowly down her spine. 'What in heaven's name are you talking about?'

Constantine made an impatient gesture with his hand. 'You will marry me, and as quickly as possible.'

There was a shocked, stunned silence as Jade stared at Constantine in disbelief. 'You must be mad,' she whispered, 'to think that I'd ever, *ever*, marry you.'

Sharon Kendrick was born in West London and has had *heaps* of jobs which include photography, nursing, driving an ambulance across the Australian desert and cooking her way around Europe in a converted double-decker bus! Without a doubt, writing is the best job she has ever had and when she's not dreaming up new heroes—some of which are based on her doctor husband!—she likes cooking, reading, theatre, drinking wine, listening to American west coast music and talking to her two children, Celia and Patrick.

Recent titles by the same author:

POTENT AS POISON

SAVAGE SEDUCTION

BY

SHARON KENDRICK

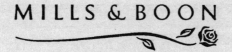

MILLS & BOON

For Tommy 'The Tiger' Crone—the amazing libel lawyer.
Thanks for your advice, Tom! And for Patti 'Pet' Crone,
great wit and great lover of 'sparkling'!

*All the characters in this book have no existence outside the imagination
of the author, and have no relation whatsoever to anyone bearing the
same name or names. They are not even distantly inspired by any
individual known or unknown to the author, and all the incidents are
pure invention.*

*MILLS & BOON and the Rose Device
are trademarks of the publisher.
Harlequin Mills & Boon Limited,
Eton House, 18-24 Paradise Road, Richmond, Surrey, TW9 1SR
This edition published by arrangement with Harlequin Enterprises B.V.*

© Sharon Kendrick 1995

ISBN 0 263 79014 2

*Set in Times Roman 11 on 12 pt
01-9506-49160 C1*

Made and printed in Great Britain

CHAPTER ONE

'OH, HELL!'

Jade made the husky imprecation as she emerged from the gin-clear water, to see that the two would-be Romeos from her home city of London had none too subtly moved themselves even closer to her towel. She shook the droplets of water from her long hair, feeling decidedly disgruntled at the prospect of having to tell them politely to go away. Again.

The droplets of water had already begun to dry on her skin. The sea had been the temperature of warm milk and as soon as she'd left it the relentless heat of the sun had started beating down on her without mercy. But that was Greece for you.

The most exquisite place she'd ever visited—with sky which was bluer than a denim shirt and sand the colour of cream and the texture of caster sugar. Add to that the heady scents of lemon mingled with pine, the wine-dark sea and the drowse-inducing mass chorus of the cicadas, and you could understand why when people discovered Greece they felt they'd stumbled on Paradise.

If only it weren't so darned hot!

She picked her way over the burning sand, and one of the Romeos sprang to his feet, the sun glinting off his fair hair.

'Hi, there, beautiful,' he said, somewhat unoriginally. 'Can I get you a drink?'

'No, thanks,' answered Jade coolly, wondering what it was about some men which made them so dense in picking up the distinctly negative vibes she was sending out.

'How about——' He raised his eyebrows suggestively, as his glance strayed to her sopping bosom, and Jade felt a sudden stirring of apprehension as she picked up her sarong to cover the tiny yellow bikini she wore.

His leer increased. '—if I rub some sun-cream into your back——?'

'How about,' came a deep and softly menacing voice from behind Jade's back, 'if you left this beach and never returned?'

And Jade whirled round to see the man from the restaurant, her throat immediately drying with the powerful impact of his darkly rugged good looks.

The Londoner was foolishly attempting resistance. 'What's it to do with you?' he demanded belligerently.

'Move away from here,' came the flat and deliberate statement, 'before I am forced to remove you myself.'

There was something in his dark eyes which brooked no argument, and the two men blanched beneath their tans. Jade watched while they gathered their few possessions up into their arms and crept away like chastened dogs.

She stayed watching them go, unaccountably excited by the man's presence, yet oddly unsure of what to do next, and it was a moment or two before she could bring herself to look up at her rescuer, who stood silently surveying her, as though it was his every right to do so. He was a stranger, yes, and yet she recognised him instantly. A man once seen, never forgotten—with the kind of fiercely dominant presence which would imprint itself on any woman's psyche, as it had on Jade's. And yet they hadn't even exchanged a word when she had seen him at the taverna yesterday...

Jade had walked into the local village to buy her provisions, and as usual it had been baking hot, absolutely *baking*. She had scooped her hand back through her thick fair hair as she'd looked over longingly at the shady canopy of lemon trees in the taverna. Through the air she could scent the lamb smouldering on the barbeque with its big bunches of thyme strewn all over it. She saw the tentacles of the octopuses dangling over a line, awaiting their ritual dousing in lemon juice before cooking. She wasn't fond of eating alone in the restaurants where tourists abounded, but this one looked full of families, and, more interestingly, full of Greeks. It must be good, she'd thought as she made her way to a shaded table.

She had ordered Greek salad, a beer and a plate of olives and was sitting enjoying them until when a small child, all dark curls and heart-shaped face, waddled over to her table. The mother called the child back in Greek, but Jade turned and shook her head, smiling, and starting to play 'peep-bo' with the toddler, who eventually climbed on to her lap and began to pick up a strand of her blonde hair in wonder. Jade pulled a funny face at the little girl who immediately giggled back as she continued to play with the blonde hair. The feeling of having the child in her arms was a new and rather enjoyable experience, and Jade couldn't help hugging her, delighted when the little girl nestled back quite happily.

Jade had sensed, rather than seen, that someone was watching her. Well, in fact, most of the restaurant were. They were enjoying the little interplay between the child and the young tourist.

But this sensation was different ... Little hairs at the back of her neck began to prickle with some nebulous excitement.

She narrowed her eyes, looking into the dim airconditioned interior of the restaurant, and through the gloom she saw a table, where a man sat surrounded by three or four others. A man in a white shirt and white jeans. A man to whom the others listened. A man with eyes as black as olives and as hard as jet. Eyes which gleamed and narrowed, frozen in a stare as they captured her gaze over the head of the child. For a stunned moment Jade stared back, unable to look away—her mouth suddenly dry, her heart pounding erratically and an unfamiliar excitement stealing over her as she gazed at the man, some unfamiliar and primitive longing sweeping over her as their eyes locked.

The man whose quietly menacing authority had driven away the two tourists, and who now stood on the beach in front of her.

The stranger was Greek; he could be nothing else. He had the proud bearing and the superbly shaped head of his ancestors. But he was tall for a Greek:

a couple of inches over six feet, she hazarded. His skin was coloured a luminously soft olive, the kind of colour which made the sales of fake tan rocket, and it gleamed very slightly, the slight sheen emphasising the ripple of muscle. His hair was as black as tar, rich and thick—a mass of unruly waves worn just slightly too long. Today he was wearing nothing but a pair of sawn-off denims; very faded and very scruffy. Those and a pair of beaten-up sandals. She swallowed at the sight of so much naked flesh on show. She should have been frightened, and yet fear was the last thing on her mind as she returned his gaze. She stared into eyes as cold and forbidding and harsh as jet. Narrow eyes that glittered; eyes which studied her with a detached and yet strangely intense appraisal which was almost intoxicating in itself.

And all of a sudden, it happened again: a replay of the sensations she had experienced the last time she had seen him. She felt her senses clamour into life, felt her heart accelerate painfully, accepted the flood of colour to her cheeks and the almost debilitating dryness of her mouth as she battled to compose herself.

'Why are you here on your own?' came his terse interrogation.

The question floored her; she was so outraged at its implicit chauvinism. 'Because I like my own company,' she answered coolly.

He didn't respond to the inference. 'Well, do not do so again.'

Jade's eyes narrowed in disbelief. 'Don't do what?'

Jet eyes glittered dangerously. 'Do not put yourself at risk. This beach is too isolated; a woman is too vulnerable.'

He spoke, she thought suddenly, like a man used to giving orders, and having them obeyed.

'Who—are you?' she asked suddenly, in a voice which seemed to have deepened by at least an octave.

He stilled, his ebony eyes narrowed with suspicion. 'You don't know?'

'Oh, for heaven's sake! If I knew then I wouldn't be asking, surely?'

'No.' He was examining her face intently, like a man newly given sight, and that slow inspection stirred some answering response deep within her. He looked, she thought dizzily, like a king—there was something stately and proud in his bearing. And yet how could he when, to judge by his appearance, he was obviously a beach bum? She had been reading far too many romantic novels on this holiday—let that be a lesson to her!

'My name is Constantine Sioulas,' he replied, in a gloriously deep voice, with only the faintest trace of an accent, and again the black eyes pierced her with their intense scrutiny.

Constantine. She tested the name in her mind; found it the most beautiful name in the whole world, which was really rather appropriate, as the man in front of her was the most beautiful man she had ever laid eyes on.

'And you?' He lifted an enquiring eyebrow. 'What is your name?'

'It's Jade,' she said rather breathlessly, as though she'd just stopped running. 'Jade Meredith.'

'Jade.' He nodded his head, thoughtfully. 'Yes. It suits you,' he pronounced. 'Your eyes are the colour of jade.'

And her cheeks were now the colour of rubies, she thought ruefully as she blushed beneath the slow scrutiny of his gaze, revelling in the approbation on his face, and yet despising herself for the way she was behaving. Why not just fall down in reverence at his knees and kiss his feet, Jade!

'No, they're not,' she lifted her chin in a defiant little gesture. 'My eyes are pale green. Jade is darker.'

He shook his head. 'Sometimes,' he contradicted. 'The Chinese say that the colour deepens and intensifies as the wearer acquires wisdom. It would be an interesting experiment—to see whether that is true.' He gave a small almost reluctant smile, like the smile of a man not used to smiling. 'Shall I buy you jade, Jade Meredith?' he said softly. 'Jewels of jade for you to wear next to that pale, pale skin? Together we could watch it growing darker day by day.'

His words were so inappropriate considering that they'd only just met. And yet he spoke them with a coolly assured confidence which only renewed the throbbing of blood to her pulse points.

'My skin isn't pale,' she protested. After nearly three weeks in the sun, it had turned a pale golden colour—she was quite proud of it!

'Most certainly it is,' he contradicted, in the rich, glowing voice overlaid with its barely discernible yet totally seductive accent. 'Pale as milk—at least when you compare it with mine.'

And at his words she found her eyes drawn irresistibly to the dark olive of his bare chest and shoulders, the strong forearms, and the equally strong thighs. Her mind responded to his suggestion with frightening clarity as she pictured her lying on a bed with him, his dark limbs tangled with hers, strong brown thigh against a thigh as pale as milk... Jade had to close her eyes briefly to blot out the tantalising image, but it didn't work.

'Shall we?' he whispered silkily.

'Shall we what?' she echoed huskily, lost in some misty erotic world of her own.

He smiled, and it was a suddenly ruthless smile. The smile, she recognised with an unquestionable certainty, of a man who was used to getting whatever it was he wanted.

'I was referring to buying the jade,' he said softly. 'But we should have to go to the mainland to do that, and I don't want to waste precious hours doing that, not when there are so many more attractive alternatives.' He smiled. 'Come, I shall walk you back to your house.'

It was most definitely an order. Jade bristled. 'That won't be necessary.'

'On the contrary,' he answered smoothly, but there was a steely quality to his voice now. 'I insist.'

Most annoyingly, she found the arrogant protectiveness in his assertion extremely attractive, but a lifetime of paying lip-service to feminism couldn't be banished overnight! She met his gaze steadily. 'I said *no*, thank you.'

'I heard what you said, but it doesn't change a thing.'

Jade shook her head from side to side in a mixture of amusement and exasperation. 'Do you always insist on getting your own way?' she demanded.

He grinned then, the most heartbreakingly gorgeous grin imaginable, and *that* was her undoing. 'I always get my own way,' he murmured. 'Though not always by insisting. I don't usually have to,' he added arrogantly.

That she *could* imagine! Jade had to try very hard to suppress a smile as she watched while he bent down to retrieve her bag and her towel and tucked them under his arm with an old-fashioned courtesy—which she *certainly* wasn't used to. She knew she was fighting a losing battle here, and what was more, she was quickly discovering that it was a battle she didn't particularly want to fight anyway. 'Then I'll take you up on your offer of walking me home,' she said. '*Thank* you.' And she saw from the slight elevation of his eyebrows that he hadn't missed the sarcastic emphasis.

'My pleasure.' His eyes were mocking. Then. 'Those tourists—do not worry about them. They shall not bother you again.'

There was something about the grim, gravelly undertone to his voice which made it sound vaguely threatening. Jade swallowed; she hadn't thought that men like this existed outside films! 'Er—you wouldn't *hurt* them?' asked Jade anxiously. 'They weren't really doing anything.'

'Because I arrived.' His eyes glittered like coals from hell. 'I saw the way he was looking at you.' He made a terse exclamation in Greek.

Jade swallowed. Had she been blasé about the danger? She saw the hard, formidable lines in the handsome face, saw the ruthless glitter in the black eyes, and she knew a fleeting feeling of sympathy for the two hapless tourists. 'You won't—*hurt* them?' she whispered again, and was relieved to see a half-smile lift the corner of his mouth.

'What did you imagine I would do—beat them into pulp?' he queried softly, and then he gave an amused smile. 'Do not be concerned, little one. I shall merely speak to them—that will serve as sufficient deterrent.'

Feeling as though she'd been caught up in a sudden time warp, Jade stared curiously up at him. 'Do you always over-react like this?' she quizzed him, forcing her voice to be light.

He shook his head. 'It is not over-reacting at all.' Some feral light sparked at the depths of the coal-dark eyes. 'In Greece, you see,' he told her, 'we are protective of our women.'

He made her feel very small and very fragile, not a bit like her rather lanky five feet nine, and Jade couldn't repress a shiver of excitement. Put like that it sounded so darkly atavistic, so—well, so thrilling, the idea of someone like this black-eyed and powerfully built man actually protecting her. Because hadn't protection been in very short supply in her life up until now?

The sun beat down on their bare heads as they walked up from the beach to the narrow track which

was masquerading as a road. Jade could see the
heat shimmering hazily upwards into the endless
blue of the sky.

'Put your hat on,' he said.

She obediently crammed the battered straw down
on her head. 'Shouldn't you?'

He gave a little shake of his head. 'I am used to
the sun.'

And hair that thick, that black, thought Jade,
would surely protect him from its fierce rays?

Lizards ran swiftly along the sun-baked road, and
he named them for her, pointing out tiny scrubby
and fragrant plants that she'd never noticed before.
His accent was entrancing; it lulled her into a
dreamy sense of well-being, and when they arrived
at last at the small house she was renting she stared
up at him, aware of the disappointment thudding
through her. I don't want this day to end, she
thought suddenly.

'You want to know what we should do next?'

Could he guess so easily what she was thinking?
she wondered dimly. Did her reluctance to see him
go show on her face? 'I...' Her voice tailed off in
hopeless confusion—*she* who everyone always said
could talk her way into the record books!

'We have a number of choices,' he mused, as
though this were the kind of bizarre conversation
he was used to conducting every day. *Was* he? 'You
could offer me some of your water and we could
sit together and drink. Or we could walk down to
the village and take some refreshment there.
Alternatively, I could initiate what we both *most*
want to do?'

And only the biggest fool in the world would have replied, 'Which is?'

'Why, to kiss, of course,' he replied, his voice a velvet caress which would have melted ice. 'That's what you want me to do, isn't it?'

Now she could feel her cheeks blanch—heaven only knew what harm this man was doing to her nervous system! He was virtually making love to her with his eyes. Jade Meredith the fearless reporter took stock of the potentially dicey situation she was in, and astonishingly *still* felt no fear. She used the gritty voice with which she'd fired questions at soap stars and the unsuspecting wives of footballers.

'Just who *are* you?' she demanded. She'd met confident men in her life before, yes, men who were arrogantly sure of their effect on women, yes—but never one who was *this* confident!

At the question, his eyes narrowed and he stilled, watching her intently from beneath dark, luxuriant brows. 'I told you.' His voice was a slumberous caress. 'My name is Constantine.'

'Yes—but...' Her voice trailed off helplessly. What could she say? Yes, you're right, you delectable man—I *do* want you to kiss me? More than I've ever wanted anything in my whole life? She was breaking every rule in the book by even standing here *listening* to him. What about all that assertiveness training she'd undergone? Did women allow men to change their minds for them? No, they most certainly did not! She gave him a conventional and dismissive nod. It was the hardest thing she'd ever had to do in her life. 'It was very kind of you to accompany me—but I think you'd better leave now.'

He smiled again. 'In time.'

He had moved closer now, and when he moved it was like poetry in motion. You could see the muscles moving in perfect symmetry beneath the olive perfection of his skin.

He really wasn't *that* tall, she reminded herself; plenty of men were taller than six feet, and she was only a few inches shorter herself. Yet there was something about the width of his shoulders and the magnificent breadth of a chest with its dark, dark whorls of hair. Something, too, about the powerful thrust of his thighs—as solidly carved as the trunk of an oak tree. All these things combined to make him seem the *biggest* man she had ever seen. She suppressed another little shiver of excitement.

He was smiling now as he let her give him the once over, again with that curiously cold smile— as though laughter was a stranger to his life. 'You aren't afraid of me.' It was a statement of fact; he sounded amused.

'No.' Perhaps that was the wrong thing to say. She knew that Greek men were notoriously old-fashioned. Would he have preferred it if she'd started backing away from him, white-faced and trembling? Oh, come *on*, Jade, she chided—why should you care what *he'd* prefer?

'Not even a little afraid?' he quizzed her softly. 'And yet you *terrify* me.'

Jade swallowed. Now he was talking in riddles. 'No, I'm not afraid of you,' she said firmly, and held her chin up stubbornly. 'But I happen to have a black belt in judo, just in case you're getting any ideas.'

This provoked a laugh, a low, rich chuckle, and Jade stupidly felt as though she'd just won the first prize in a raffle. 'Very commendable,' he remarked. 'But you know that your—black belt—in judo wouldn't do you any good at all?'

Such arrogance! Such *amazing* arrogance! 'Let me enlighten you,' she said quite calmly, which was astonishing considering how fast her heart was hammering away in her chest. 'Size has nothing to do with it.'

'Oh, really?' he teased softly, and her comment became something else completely. The black eyes glittered with mischief, and Jade coloured to the roots of her hair. *Now* what had she said?

'I mean comparative size,' she said firmly, refusing to back down or be intimidated. 'You are taller and obviously stronger than I am, but judo isn't about brute strength—it's all to do with control and balance, of observing your opponent and waiting for the right opportunity.'

'I know. And that isn't what I meant.'

'Oh? And just what did you mean? You implied that I'd be unable to defeat you.'

'Absolutely,' he said softly. 'And do you know why? Because I think that once we made contact...whoosh!' He lifted the palms of his hands in front of that magnificent bare chest in a flamboyant gesture that an Englishman could never have got away with.

Jade's heart had renewed its hammering. She shouldn't be letting him talk to her like this; didn't

Greek men notoriously think that Englishwomen were easy? Well, he was about to discover that Jade Meredith was not among that merry band of women who fell swooning into the arms of handsome islanders for two weeks of holiday bliss before being put firmly on the plane with a load of lies about writing. 'Is this your normal chat-up line?' she asked cuttingly. 'Because it if is I'd give you nought out of ten for subtlety!'

The dark brows knitted together. 'Chat-up line,' he mused. 'Considering that English is one of the most perfect and complex of languages, that phrase is rather—inelegant, wouldn't you say?'

It was rather shaming that someone to whom English was not a first language could express himself so eloquently, Jade thought with a touch of irritation. She had expected that to put him in his place, not to start some highbrow discussion about semantics!

The ebony brows remained knitted together. 'And if we're going to continue this—*fascinating* discussion—might I suggest that we do it in a little more comfort?' He looked pointedly at the table where the empty water jug sat. 'Shall we sit down?'

Excitement vyed with prudence. 'Why should we? I don't know you,' she said stubbornly.

'But you know enough to know that I won't hurt you?'

Jade stared at him. Enough, yes, to know that he would never physically hurt her, but . . . as she looked into those glittering black eyes, observed the slash of jaw and the high cheekbones, she suddenly felt some terrifying fear icing her skin. A knowledge that, yes, this magnificent creature with the cold smile and the eyes of jet *could* hurt her. That through him she could learn the real meaning of pain; indescribable, unbearable pain... She started to shake uncontrollably, a violent tremor which ran through her body like wildfire.

He saw her tremble. A warm hand was placed on her chilled forearm and she felt his strength like a warm embrace.

'Fear not—I will not hurt you,' he said quietly.

You will, she thought suddenly. Oh, this was *ridiculous*! Had three weeks in Greece had turned her into a clairvoyant? She shook him away inelegantly, but he captured her hand in his, raising it to his mouth where it stayed just centimetres away from the proud curve of his lips.

'Do you not know that in Greece it is customary to offer the traveller refreshment?'

Her breathing was inhibited, shallow, painful. She awaited the brush of his mouth on her hand.

In vain.

His eyes gleamed and he let her hand go, but somehow he had regained supremacy, and Jade was angry. Angry with herself for wanting him to press his lips on to her hand, and angry that he had not chosen to! And she wasn't sending him away with him thinking that she was some kind of desperado! She straightened her shoulders and gave her most English smile, spoke in her most chillingly polite tone.

'Then you must sit down and have a drink.'

'Thank you.' In response, he deepened his accent, his eyes sparking with mischief, and Jade found

herself wanting to giggle. So much for icy politeness!

'I'll fill the jug and fetch another glass,' she said
hastily.

And she scrambled inside as he pulled out one
of the wooden chairs, which now looked hopelessly
insubstantial if expected to accommodate that large,
muscular frame.

Jade filled the jug with water and ice and found
the glass with fingers which were still trembling,
her eyes lifting reluctantly to the small spotted
mirror which hung on the whitewashed walls. A
wild-eyed, fey stranger stared back at her. Her pale
green eyes were almost unrecognisable as her own,
the colour almost completely obscured by the deep
ebony of two dilated and glittering pupils. Her
mouth looked swollen and throbbing and redder
than usual—had she been chewing it while talking
to him? she wondered. Even her hair—baby-fine
but masses of it—which she hadn't had a chance
to brush since he'd disturbed her; it had dried into
a thick, pale cloud—shimmered like an uncontrol-
lable halo around her head. The sun had bleached
it almost blonde. Did Constantine, she thought
suddenly, like women with blonde hair?

She took the jug and glass back outside, half
afraid that he might have disappeared, but he
hadn't. He had spread those long olive legs beneath
the table and was watching her return.

Walking suddenly seemed a skill she hadn't yet
acquired, and she would have stumbled if a strong
hand hadn't shot out and caught her. She managed
to get the jug down on the table, but the tumbler

slipped from her grasp; the sound of the glass shattering on the grey stone of the courtyard sounding piercingly loud to her ears.

'Oh, hell! Now look what you've made me do,' said Jade unreasonably, and, crouching down, she began gingerly to pick up the larger fragments.

He was beside her in an instant. 'Be careful,' he told her, but it was too late, a shard had pierced her forefinger, and crimson blood began to well and to drop in dark starry splashes on to the grey stone.

Her finger went up to her mouth, but he deliberately took it before it reached its destination, the black eyes fixed on hers as he put it into his mouth and sucked the blood away.

If there hadn't been glass all around them, Jade thought that she would have keeled over. She felt the blood drain from her face as she stared into the night-dark eyes.

'You—shouldn't have done that,' she said shakily.

He relieved the pressure, but her finger stayed firmly in the hot, moist cavern of his mouth. 'Why not?'

'It's dangerous,' she managed. 'Blood...'

He shook his head, as if he understood her meaning perfectly. 'I think not.'

'How can you know?' she demanded breathlessly. 'We've only just met.'

His eyes met hers. 'I know,' he said softly.

Another slow and deliberate suck; it was the most erotic thing that had ever happened to her in her life—and then he took the finger from his mouth, examined it and held it up for her inspection. 'The

flow is stemmed,' he pronounced, and something
in the formality of this statement, spoken with all
the solemnity of a Victorian surgeon, instead of the
more modern 'it's stopped bleeding', made Jade's
lips twitch in amusement.

He saw the movement, and raised his eyebrows.
'What?'

'You have a very formal way of speaking,' she
said honestly. 'But your English is absolutely
superb.'

He inclined his head. 'And so it should be. I grew
up with it as my second language.'

She shook her head, as if bemused by what
was happening. 'Are you always like this—
Constantine?' She said his name experimentally for
the first time. Her tongue had to protrude a little
in order to pronounce it properly, in the slightly
lisping Greek manner. She liked saying it, liked the
way his eyes flared as he watched her tongue snake
out and then back in again.

'Like—what?'

Jade stared back into the glittering black eyes,
realising that she actually felt as though she were
high on something—if this feeling was ever mar-
keted, the world would go into total chaos! 'So
darned assertive!' she answered crisply.

He looked surprised. 'But naturally. Are not all
men supposed to be assertive? The dominant ones?'

She smiled. 'That's not what the feminists would
say.'

'Ah! The feminists! You are one of these?' He
ran his eyes lazily over the bright and filmy covering

of her sarong, at the cloud of blonde hair. 'I don't think so,' he observed.

Jade could not let that pass. 'You think that I couldn't possibly be a feminist because I haven't got cropped hair and am not wearing dungarees?'

A light flared in his eyes. 'But those are your words, Jade,' he said softly. 'Not mine. No, I made the comment because I could imagine you soft, and pliant, loving and giving. *Very* feminine, but not a feminist. There is a subtle difference, you know.'

Jade realised that she was letting him get away with statements she would have emphatically disagreed with if she'd been back at home in England. Persuasive kind of guy. She tried again. 'But men being so dominant and assertive,' she said, 'it isn't really the modern way.'

'But I,' he answered proudly, 'am not a modern man. At heart all Greeks are ruled by the very same passions which have existed since the beginning of time.'

This was totally new, uncharted and terribly exciting territory, men talking quite openly of passion. Jade shivered.

'But perhaps,' he said deliberately, 'you are not used to assertive men?'

Oh, but she was—she most certainly was! But there was a world of difference between the way all the men at her office behaved, and the way that Constantine was behaving. Her editor rode roughshod over all the staff. However, perhaps that was less like assertion, and more like bullying! Certainly there was none of this man's cool assurance in her boss's behaviour.

'Well, are you?' he persisted.

She wasn't used to men at all, not in the sense that he meant. Which was probably why she was responding in such a *pathetic* way towards this particular man. Men had been deliberately put on ice until the career which had meant so much to her had had a chance to develop properly—the career which she was now thinking of chucking in because she was so disillusioned with it. A cynic already—and at the tender age of twenty!

She stared into the black eyes, blinked, then looked down at the thick fragments of glass which glittered by their feet. Mostly from a desire to steer the conversation away from her shameful lack of experience with the opposite sex, she began to turn away. 'I'd better go and fetch a dustpan and brush——'

'No.'

There he went again, dishing out the orders! Jade stared up at him, half in anger, half in admiration, marvelling that it actually felt extraordinarily *good* to be around such a masterful man. Shame on her!

'You put some covering on your finger. Go! I will deal with the glass.'

She found herself obeying him without question. In the tiny bedroom she found the box of Elastoplast she had brought with her from England, and, after removing the wrapping, she shakily applied one to her thumb. She could hear him moving around in the kitchen, presumably looking for the dustpan and brush. She didn't doubt for a moment that he'd find it!

She wondered fleetingly whether she had a touch of sunstroke. Surely *normal* women of her age didn't allow half-clothed perfect strangers the run of their house? And yet, given the outstanding attraction of the man, she didn't feel in the least bit threatened. She examined her finger carefully. Well, that wasn't entirely true. She felt a threat, all right, but it had absolutely nothing to do with thinking that he might be some mad axeman. It was more an interested kind of wondering just what *would* happen if she caught him in a judo stranglehold. That expressive little 'whoosh' sound he'd made . . . implying . . . mmmm . . .

She went outside to find him disposing of the last of the glass. It was strange to see such a self-proclaimed non-modern man doing it so competently, and yet to see Constantine brushing up the fragments of glass . . . it almost *emphasised* his masculinity, rather than detracting from it. Confusing, she thought fleetingly. He'd talked about the man assuming the dominant role, and had teased her about feminists, and yet he didn't seem to mind lending a hand. Interesting.

As she appeared, he straightened up.

'I will wrap it up tightly in newspaper,' he instructed. 'So no more cut fingers.'

Jade nodded, acknowledging the perverse sinking of her heart. There was something of the farewell in the way he spoke. Surely he wasn't going?

She ventured a smile. 'You didn't have your drink.'

'No matter. It is time I was going.'

She had been right. 'Yes.' Disappointment crept through her veins like a debilitating drug.

'I shall collect you at seven.'

'Collect me?' squeaked Jade, only keeping the excitement from her voice with the most monumental of efforts. 'What for?'

The mouth moved again in its curious smile. 'Why, for dinner, of course.'

'I'm having dinner with you?'

'Of course. Don't you want to?'

Which he asked with all the casual arrogance of a man who knew damned well that of course she wanted to have dinner with him! Who wouldn't? Jade had never experienced this overwhelming attraction before; it made you weak and it made you powerless. And she wasn't really sure whether she liked the feeling or not. Besides which—wouldn't it be totally foolhardy to go tripping off with him? Why should he *presume* that she'd just drop everything and have dinner with him? And what happened after dinner? What did he expect? Did he assume that because she was English she was going to fall into bed with him?

'What makes you think I'll say yes?'

He gave a slow smile, then raised that olive-skinned hand to her face. 'These,' he said softly, as he indicated her eyes. 'They give me one answer and one answer only. Then this——' And a finger brushed negligently over the bow of her mouth. 'It trembles with anticipation. And——' and here the eyes changed, the spark in their ebony depths becoming a feverish flame '—there are other outward

signs of how much you want to see me again, but
we will not go into those. Not now.'

She was innocent, but she knew exactly what he
meant. She had been unsuccessfully trying to ignore
the hot tingling as her tiny breasts thrust against
the still damp material of her bikini top. The tips
were as painfully hard as metal and yet the pain
was bearable, pleasurable even, and her eyelids
dropped to hide her confusion. She knew what she
wanted, what she clamoured for. She clamoured for
his touch. And, oh, heavens—wasn't it desperately
shameful to want a complete stranger to touch her
intimately? To run those strong brown fingers all
over her pale breasts and to linger on the soft swell
of her belly? Her cheeks burned.

He moved his hand beneath her chin, so that their
eyes were locked on a collision course. In his eyes
she could see reflected the febrile glitter in hers.
'I'll pick you up at seven,' he said huskily.

It wasn't fair, thought Jade. For a man to wield
so much power over women—all women, she recognised with a violently jealous flare. I'll bet he
never has to ask twice, she thought, with a sudden
inexplicable anger, and was determined that in this,
at least—she would be different. 'No, I can't,' she
said stubbornly and immediately saw a momentary
flare of irritation before it was replaced by a questioning look.

'You're busy?'

'That's right.'

'No, you're not,' he said quietly.

'Why, of all the——'

But he cut her off with an arrogant shake of his black head. 'Listen to me, Jade,' he said quietly. 'You return to England shortly, yes?'

'In three days,' something compelled her to tell him.

'So.' The hand was still holding her face with gentle strength. 'We can either play foolish little games with each other. Or...'

'Or?'

His eyes narrowed; his expression was rueful— as though he was reluctant to complete the sentence.

'Or we can follow our hearts,' he said simply.

If anyone else had said it, she would have told them that they were being ridiculously corny, that no one said things like that and meant them, and yet it was the most romantic thing she'd ever encountered, and Jade felt a warm glow suffuse every pore of her body.

She stared up at him, a lost cause for assertive womanhood. 'OK,' she said, giving him a faltering smile as she looked into his eyes. 'I'll see you at seven.'

'Until seven,' he said, his hand falling from her face as he strode swiftly from the courtyard.

CHAPTER TWO

IN THE five hours until Constantine collected her, Jade experienced just about every mood-swing in the book. What the hell was she playing at? He could be *anyone*—anyone at all!

What did she know about him?

Absolutely nothing.

Well, that wasn't *quite* true. She knew his name and his nationality. Knew instinctively that he had a million times more experience than she had. And she also knew that he was the most devastating man she'd ever set eyes on.

But what was he thinking about her? Was he down in the village even now, boasting to his friends that the English girl had agreed with insulting speed to go out with a man she scarcely knew? Did men respect women who capitulated quite so easily?

Jade sighed. Suddenly, it became very important that he *did* respect her. I don't want him thinking I'm like this with everyone, she thought gloomily. But if she tried to tell him *that*—then wouldn't it bolster his already appallingly healthy ego?

She sighed again.

She didn't really have any option but to go. She didn't know where he lived, so there was no way she could duck out now. She supposed that she could always tell him that she'd changed her mind when he arrived at seven to collect her.

And yet...

Somehow she didn't see that as a realistic scenario at all. For a start, she *wanted* to see him, so her words would have the hollow ring of insincerity. And secondly, she couldn't really see him letting her get away with fobbing him off. She imagined him taking her ruthlessly into his arms, black eyes glimmering like a pirate, to kiss away every single objection she could think of.

Jade shivered as she walked into her bedroom. She would go, but her choice of garment would be crucial. Something demure, something which would definitely not give him the wrong idea...

The only trouble was that the clothes chosen for holidays in baking hot destinations tended to be all the things which *weren't* demure. Light, filmy fabrics. Lots of bare flesh on show. Oh, heck. Jade surveyed the six or so dresses she'd brought with her. She tried them all on, and each one in a different way made her achingly aware of her own body, unless... she stared at her naked reflection... unless Constantine had done that. Because never before had she been so conscious of the soft swell of her breasts above the slender line of her waist. Breasts which tightened just at the very thought of him. She remembered his comment about pale, pale skin when compared to his, and once again, with a lucidity which was shocking, given her inexperience, Jade closed her eyes and pictured her breasts laid bare. With a dark head bending to take each one in turn, to suckle with delectable sweetness as the dark waves of his hair teased and tickled her flesh...

Jade stared in the spotted mirror in horror, to see her nipples rucking into tight twin peaks, and she drew her hands over them to cover the shockingly sensual image with her palms, but even that didn't help, because she found herself wanting them to be *his* hands touching her, and she turned away from the mirror, sick with disgust.

But, after she had finally chosen an outfit, she managed to calm down. If she hadn't trusted him, then she'd never have accepted a date with him. And though he might *look* all strong and compelling charm, she also knew that the Greeks were courteous and charming to visitors. There would never need to be attentions forced... Frankly, she doubted whether he'd had to use an ounce of persuasion in his life. Which left it up to *her* to modify the pace.

He was bang on time.

Jade was sitting in the courtyard, reading, when his shadow fell over the pages of her book, and she looked up, unable to keep the smile off her face as she registered his narrow-eyed appreciation of her appearance.

'Hi,' she said softly.

'Hello,' he echoed. His voice was equally soft, and there was another brief flash of appraisal in his eyes as his gaze swept over her.

She wore a white sleeveless silk T-shirt, together with an ankle-length skirt in layers of white, swirling voile. The starkness of the colour emphasised the pale golden glow of her skin. At her waist was a soft leather belt of dark green, with an intricately scrolled silver clasp. On her feet were strappy leather sandals in the same green. She had left her hair loose, to fall down her back in a pale waterfall, and at her ears and throat and wrist she wore heavy and intricate silver jewellery.

'You look wonderful,' he said quietly.

She took in the snowy white of his shirt, tucked into dark, tapered trousers. His hair was still damp from the shower, falling into tendrils around his beautifully shaped head. 'So do you,' she said honestly.

He looked slightly bemused for a moment, and then he laughed, a deep and rich and glorious sound. 'Do you know,' he mused, 'that's the first time a woman's ever said that to me?'

Her cheeks hot, she stared down at her pink-painted toenails, wondering what in the world had made her come out with something like that. His women usually played it cool, obviously, she thought, and a spear of jealousy shot through her. 'I don't know what came into me—I don't usually say things like that either,' she said, her tone more defensive than she'd intended.

But his voice was warm, caressing, forcing her to meet his eyes. 'Don't apologise. That's the magic of the island,' he said softly. 'Working her spell on young lovers.'

Oh, lord. He *had* got the wrong idea. Well, it was about time she put him on the right track. Jade took a deep breath. 'I think you're assuming rather a lot, Constantine,' she said stiffly. 'I've agreed to have dinner with you—that's all, and I have absolutely no intention of becoming your lover. And if that's what you had in mind for the end of the evening, then perhaps you'd better leave right now.'

His eyes darkened, glistened like two fragments of hell's coal. She saw a muscle begin to work with ominous regularity in the side of the olive cheek, saw his mouth tighten into a hard slash, and then she *did* know the meaning of fear, saw suddenly the face of a ruthless man behind the shatteringly handsome mask. All power and strength.

'Is that what you think?' he gritted in a low, furious voice. 'That I am one of these men who expects sex as a form of payment for buying a woman dinner?'

He looked more than angry, she thought, he looked *furious*, as if she'd deeply offended his code of honour.

'Of course I don't!' she said hurriedly. 'It's just——'

'Just?'

She lifted her shoulders in bewilderment. 'I didn't mean to insult you. I don't know what I meant. When you made that remark about lovers...I didn't want you to think...'

'I didn't,' he said simply. 'And as for your confusion—do you think I don't feel it too? Do you think this happens to *me* every day of the week?'

'What?'

But he shook his head. 'Enough. All this talk on an empty stomach. Come. Let's go and eat.'

She fell into step beside him, giving him her hand when he held his out, walking down the dusty path towards the village, safe within the warmth of his grasp. Sinking into the distance, the giant dinner-plate of a sun flooded them with a rich, crimson light and it felt like being at the centre of some glowing and infernal jewel.

They walked into the village, past the restaurant where she'd seen him yesterday.

He saw the inquisitive rise of her eyebrows. 'There is little enough privacy in the village,' he explained. 'But even less there.'

'Oh? And why's that?'

He smiled down at her. 'My family owns it.'

So—he was in the restaurant business with his family. And he didn't want her to meet them! Some little English girl he was ashamed to be seen with. She began to pull her hand away, but he wouldn't let her, instead stopped still on the dusty track and turned her to face him.

'What's wrong?'

Peculiarly, it was too important to her to lie about. 'Of course, if you don't *want* me to meet your family——'

'*Agape mou*,' he laughed softly, 'there is a way that a man can behave with a woman which in Greece would have his family drawing up a wedding list.'

Her heart sounded very loud in her ears. 'And what way's that?'

'Never taking his eyes off her. Not wanting to eat. Not wanting to do anything other than kiss her and make love to her. I've seen it happen to other men before; but never to me. The way I intend to behave with you tonight, Jade,' he finished with quiet emphasis. 'And I would prefer not to have an audience.'

The darkness was falling and it camouflaged her soft rise in colour, the sharp little intake of breath. It had sounded as if... As if what? As if he was falling in love with her? As she was with him? Oh, stop it, *stop* it, she thought shakily. 'But surely,' she questioned, 'all the restaurants will be crowded tonight—it's the height of the season.'

'Wait and see,' he promised.

In a dream she walked with him to the outside of the village, to a white building which looked out over the blue and green fragrant hills, the stars beginning to glimmer in the indigo velvet of the sky.

A waiter led them to a terrace, where rose-coloured candles burned incandescently on each table against the ever-darkening night. This restaurant was obviously much more upmarket than the others in the village, thought Jade as Constantine held her chair out for her, because crisp white tablecloths matched the beautifully pleated damask napkins.

There was wine already chilling in the ice-bucket, and Jade accepted a glass, together with the leather-bound menu, her eyes wide with confusion.

'Where *is* everyone?' she whispered. 'Why are *we* the only customers?'

He smiled, his teeth showing very white in the olive darkness of his face. 'Because, as I told you, I wanted privacy.'

'But how——?'

His eyes narrowed. 'The proprietor owes me a favour,' he said implacably, and Jade once again got an overwhelming feeling of a toughness emanating from the man who sat opposite her.

She sipped at her drink nervously. 'You mean—that we've got the whole restaurant to ourselves? As a favour to you?'

He gave a little nod. 'I do.'

'It must have been a very big favour.' In Jade's world, people just didn't *do* things like that. But this was, after all, Greece. Many parts of it a still very fundamental world, with values light-years away from the superficial mores of life in the highly developed west, or even from life in its capital, Athens. Without knowing why, goosebumps chilled her arms, even though the night air was warm and soft on her skin.

'Some day I'll tell you,' he smiled, and handed her one of the menus.

'Some day'...?

Did his words imply that they had some sort of future together?

Jade tried very hard to concentrate on the choice of food—grilled fish and meat mainly—and to stop reading things into what he was saying.

Constantine spoke in rapid Greek to the waiter, of which she understood not one word—bar his name, Kris, and moments later they were brought a dish containing the tiny hors-d'oeuvres known as *mezes*.

'So——' He popped a green olive into his mouth and chewed it. 'Tell me what such a beautiful woman is doing holidaying on her own?'

Jade looked at him suspiciously, scared that he was making fun of her. 'Very funny,' she said.

He raised his eyebrows. 'What?'

'I'm not beautiful,' she told him, her green eyes glittering with a challenge that dared him to lie to her.

He drew his brows together. 'On the contrary. I'm being deadly serious. You are tall enough to model and you are extremely slender, almost too slender—I can see that I may need to feed you up. But truly, you are beautiful,' he stated. 'Quite astonishingly so.'

Beautiful? *Her*? Jade was sensible enough to know her good points and her bad points, but no one had ever called her beautiful before, and in common with others who had had a fragmented childhood her body image was poor. True, she was tall, but she'd always considered herself a bit of a beanpole, and yes, she found it almost impossible to put on weight—which was beneficial in a society so obsessed by thinness. But her mouth was much too wide for conventional beauty, and her narrow slanting eyes did not have the classic wide-eyed appeal which men were said to find attractive. Plus, in England—given the nature of the sexist men she worked with—she tended to sublimate her femininity with her hair scraped back into a sensible plait, and clothes which were designed to be functional but nothing more than that. She supposed that on *this* holiday she had allowed herself to relax the normal severity with which she dressed. But beautiful? Did he say that to all the girls? she wondered.

However, even this sobering thought couldn't abate her delight, and Jade found herself smiling

at Constantine like an idiot. This was ridiculous—
one compliment and she was like putty in his hands!

'So,' he continued. 'Tell me why you're here on
your own?'

'I needed a break,' she said honestly.

'A break from what?'

Jade twirled the stem of her glass round and
round between her fingers, watching the conden-
sation trickle slowly down the side.

Tricky. She wondered just how much to tell him.

True, Constantine was a Greek, whose family
owned a tiny taverna on a small Greek island—he
might not even have *heard* of the *Daily View*. But
what if he had?

After she'd won the Young Journalist competition launched by the *Daily View*, they had offered
her a job as reporter—a job she had accepted with
eager gratitude, given the cut-throat world of journalism. *Then* she'd been proud to tell people that
she worked on Britain's best-selling tabloid newspaper. But that was before she'd discovered what
most people actually thought of the *Daily View*.

They despised it.

Time and time again, when she had explained
who she worked for, she had seen an expression of
scorn come into the faces of people who viewed
tabloid writers as total drunks with no morals. So,
in the end, she had stopped telling them. It made
for an easier life.

She stared into Constantine's dark eyes and made
her decision. This was one evening out of her
lifetime, she reasoned; an evening scented with
magic which would soon become nothing more than

a distant memory. This was total fantasy, so why taint it with the bitter taste of reality?

She saw that he was waiting for her answer and gave a little shrug. 'I just wanted a break,' she said carefully.

'A break from something in particular?' he probed. 'A man perhaps?'

Now he really *had* got the wrong end of the stick! 'Heavens, no!' she exclaimed fervently, unaware of the small smile he gave to this. 'Nothing like that! I meant a break from city life.'

He sipped at his drink and surveyed her curiously. 'You're very young?'

'I'm twenty,' she answered, and then, more tentatively, because it suddenly seemed terribly important, 'And you?'

'Thirty.' There was a glimmer of a smile. Had he guessed what she'd been thinking? 'That is a good gap, yes? Ten years?' He stared across the table at her moonwashed hair, raising his glass to his lips. 'So tell me—what do you think of my island?'

'You don't actually happen to own it, do you?' she joked.

'You must forgive me yet another possessive Greek statement,' he said implacably.

'I love your island,' she said simply. 'I've never relaxed so much in my life. I've spent my whole time being thoroughly lazy, swimming every day——'

'I know.'

She looked into his eyes. 'How can you know?'

'Because I've watched you. Looking like a mermaid with that yellow hair, those mysterious green eyes, that secretive smile.'

'You were—*watching* me?' she asked, appalled at the way her heart galloped into action.

He nodded. 'I was your guardian angel. Like today. Didn't you know?'

Jade shook her head. 'No.' Thank heavens she *hadn't* gone topless!

'And do you mind?'

'I don't know really. Isn't it a loss of the privacy you were so keen to preserve this evening?'

He looked at her thoughtfully. 'Perhaps. But I couldn't stay away,' he said simply, as though this excused everything, then popped another olive into his mouth and smiled. 'Let's order.'

Jade was relieved to have something relatively ordinary to do to keep her attention from the lunatic thoughts which were buzzing around her head. For Constantine seemed to possess some powerful quality she'd never encountered in a man before. Something which touched and matched some deep, dark longing inside her, offering her a glimpse of a passionate side to her nature she hadn't dreamed existed.

And she already suspected—no, she *knew*, that this—relationship, if you could call it that, threatened to get out of control very quickly. And she knew what out of control meant. Shocking though it was, she wanted this arrogant and handsome man she'd only just met to make love to her. She wanted to taste the pleasures that she instinctively knew that only he could offer her. But no one in their right mind would allow such a wish to become reality. After all, what possible future could a London-based journalist have with a restaurant proprietor who lived on a distant Greek island?

None.

Jade forced herself to apply her attention towards the food, which was surprisingly good and simple. They ate Greek salad, scarlet with tomatoes and white with feta cheese and black with olives, with strong olive oil drizzled all over it. 'And what do you do in England?' he pursued.

'Oh, it's just a boring old typing job,' she said vaguely. True, although she knew she was being economical with the truth—but what if *he* had the rest of the world's prejudices about tabloid journalists? The evening would be ruined before it had even got started. She dipped some bread into the olive oil, then ate it. 'And how about you? Are you a waiter at your family's restaurant?'

He paused with the fork halfway to his mouth, and the corners of his mouth twitched before he laid it down on his plate. 'Sometimes,' he said. 'And I help them—balance the books—as the English say.'

She looked around her and breathed in the scented air. 'It must be a heavenly place to live,' she told him.

'Oh, it is,' he agreed gravely. 'Indeed, it is.'

And after that the evening seemed to get better and better.

'You have brothers and sisters?' he asked.

Jade took a large swallow of wine. 'No. And you?'

Something indefinable came into his eyes as he shook his head. 'Just a brother. And a——' He hesitated, momentarily. 'Step-sister. But I like big families. And you?'

It was something she had never, ever considered until this moment. Children were somewhere off in a hazy, rosy future which she'd somehow never imagined happening, not to her. She had never given much thought to children, but tonight she *was*, and she had the strongest suspicion that he was, too. She remembered their eyes meeting over the head of the tousle-haired toddler, of that spark which had flown between the two of them; a spark born out of mutual need and understanding. But what on earth was she admitting to? That she wanted to stay here and have his children? To live on a Greek island with one of its inhabitants? She, who had always been so ambitious, so determined to succeed?

Yes, yes, *yes*!

'What's the matter?' He interrupted her silence. 'You don't approve of big families?'

As the truth dawned on her, it felt like coming home. 'Oh, no—I absolutely *love* them!'

He smiled, his eyes gently sweeping over her shining eyes, her dazzling smile. 'I'm glad,' he said softly.

Never had a meal seemed to take so long; Jade had no appetite for it. She remembered having odd dates where the meal had assumed the greatest importance because the man she was out with had seemed so dull. And yet tonight—delicious as the *barbouni* smelt, and however sweet and succulent its flesh, she couldn't wait to be away from here, to be some place alone with Constantine, to taste the delights of his lips, discover the safety of his arms.

At last they were away and walking back down the dusty road, until they reached her cottage. He hadn't tried to kiss her, not once, and when they stood outside her door Jade turned to him in confusion.

He nodded as he read her eyes. 'Not tonight, *agape mou*.' And then he said something in Greek softly beneath his breath.

'What did you just say?'

He gave a soft laugh. '*Epikindhinos*. It means dangerous. Just like you. There is danger in the witchy slant of your eyes, in the pale waterfall of your hair. And the dangers that lie within those dark red lips, and all the secret places of your body—ah! They are too manifold even to dare to imagine!'

Jade found herself laughing at his extravagance; somehow he had turned the tension into humour, and she found herself admiring him for it. The first man who hadn't tried to leap on her on a first date. Typical that it should be the only one she'd ever wanted to!

He picked up her hand and carried it to his lips, placed a fleeting kiss there. 'We shall spend the day together tomorrow.'

'Doing what?'

There was a fleetingly ruthless smile. 'Doing our best not to make love. Being—circumspect. That is what we must do. And now, my golden-haired angel—go and sleep. Dream of me until I arrive tomorrow morning.'

Not surprisingly, she *did* dream of him, and wonderful dreams they were, too—but the reality of the real man who arrived the following morning at eight o'clock far outshone the dream version.

He spent three days doing exactly what he had said he would do—being circumspect.

Jade was flattered; and frustrated.

She knew how much he wanted her, and how much she ached just to have him kiss her, but he didn't.

Instead, he took her snorkelling, took her round the island on the back of his motorcycle. They swam and they picnicked. He taught her elementary Greek and backgammon—he beat her—and she taught him some very corny jokes and Scrabble—she beat him. She never met a member of his family, and he seemed as reluctant to discuss his 'other' life as she was, and Jade found it very easy to simply put her London life into a compartment of her mind, and forget all about it.

For those three days they were together from early morning until midnight, and it was as though no world existed for them bar the island. There was no past; the future they did not dare to touch upon; instead there was just the glorious and golden present.

And then her last day arrived. They spent a morning snorkelling off a beach which was almost deserted, lunching again in the small restaurant which had become their regular haunt and where

Kris, the owner, spent the whole time virtually bowing to Constantine.

He seemed terribly well respected, thought Jade, as she accepted the *metaliko nero*—mineral water— he handed her.

But as the day wore on, they both grew noticeably quieter and eventually he took her back to the cottage.

'Where shall we eat tonight?'

It was hard to be enthusiastic. Impossible, in fact. 'I don't mind.'

'It's your last night,' he said, and there was a strange, almost savage note to his voice.

'Yes.' She stared up, found herself mesmerised by the ebony glitter of his eyes. She saw that a pulse worked frantically in the side of his cheek. Her own pulse hammered; her mouth dried like dust and she found herself moistening her lips with the tip of her tongue, then blushed scarlet when his eyes narrowed as they watched the movement, afraid that he would interpret it as one of deliberate provocation. Embarrassed, she made to turn away, but he stopped her with one strong olive hand on the bare flesh of her upper arm.

'Where do you want to go tonight?' he repeated.

There was a pause. 'Nowhere,' she said quietly and honestly.

'We can't stay here,' he said, almost savagely.

'Why not?'

'You know why not.'

'OK, then, Constantine—you tell me where *you'd* like to go tonight?'

There was a long pause. 'Nowhere,' he said softly. His voice was unsteady as he spoke. 'I think that our days of being circumspect are numbered, don't you, *agape mou*?'

She was aware of the enormity of the question. Head bent, she nodded silently.

'Look at me,' he whispered. 'Jade. *Please.*'

Slowly, slowly, she raised her head. His eyes were dark.

'I'm almost afraid to kiss you,' he said huskily.

'I can't imagine you being afraid of anything, Constantine.'

'Not even of losing my sanity, my reason?'

'Then you'd better not kiss me,' she said firmly. 'I don't want to be responsible for—*oh*,' the gasp became an exultant little sigh as he locked her in his arms, his heart thundering against her breast. Breathlessly, she waited with longing for his lips.

'Not kiss you?' It was a soft, mocking taunt. 'I must. If only to tell myself that this is all some foolish fantasy...'

His head came down and his mouth imprisoned her in a sensual trap from which she never wanted to escape. He tasted of wine, and of honey. He tasted of man, primitive man; hot, hungry, and very, very aroused.

His kiss was soft and sweet, cajoling her response, so that her lips opened for him, and she heard him make a murmured appraisal as he licked his way into her mouth. She opened her mouth wider, felt their tongues link together as the kiss deepened with an intensity which was shattering.

Jade could feel her breasts tingling as she lifted her arms up with a helpless sigh to lock them around his neck, her fingers drifting upwards to entwine themselves in the black richness of his hair.

He lifted his mouth away from hers and stared down into her upturned face, the feverish glitter in his eyes as bright as moonlight. Very slowly and deliberately, he pulled her closer, so that she could feel the shocking potency of his arousal.

Except that it did not shock her; it thrilled her immeasurably. She wanted that; him. Deep within her. She wanted their bodies locked in the most basic physical communion of all. She stared back at him, rocked at the strength of her feelings, her eyes dark, her lips trembling.

'Jade,' he said softly, and now the accent was more pronounced than she'd ever heard it. 'Do you know how much I want to make love to you?'

'Yes,' she answered quietly. There was the evidence of that powerfully hard shaft which pushed against her lower belly through the filmy white voile of her dress—but she could have read his desire just as easily in the incandescent depths of his night-dark eyes. And his mouth, too, was trembling, as though what was happening to them had startled him, too.

'I want to touch your breasts,' he whispered against her mouth. 'To touch them until I know them better than you do,' and before she could say or do a thing he had pulled the silk T-shirt from beneath her belt, and was peeling it off and over her head, so that she stood before him, naked to the waist, her skin gilded golden and crimson by the dying light of the sun, her hair as bright and as glimmering as the stars which would later appear.

He just gazed down at her breasts, as if committing them to memory, nodding his head as he did so. 'I knew that you wore nothing beneath,' he murmured. 'Your breasts are small, yes, but all day long they have been aching, haven't they, Jade?'

She swallowed. This was madness. 'Yes,' she whispered.

'Waiting for my touch,' he murmured, and he cupped one small mound in the palm of his hand, his thumb reaching out to stroke with tantalising skill at the stiffened nub of her nipple.

'Oh!' breathed Jade, on a strangled note of disbelief, and her knees buckled beneath her, but he caught her, pulling her roughly into his arms, his mouth against hers.

'Let's go to bed,' he said, almost harshly.

Jade's eyelids fluttered open as she sought to reason with herself. She was alone in the middle of nowhere, with a man intent on making love to her. And she couldn't, she realised, on a shuddering sigh...she couldn't stop him; even if she wanted to.

And she didn't want to.

She was on fire with some strange magic, caught up in the throes of a spell so powerful that she felt she would die if he left her.

Was there, she wondered foggily as he picked her up and carried her into the cottage—was there such a thing as love at first sight?

Yes! she thought fiercely, and she reached up for him, and he dropped his mouth to hers again,

kissing her as he walked until they were in her
bedroom.

He laid her on the bed while he shrugged his way
out of the white shirt he wore, and she saw the
heaving of the powerful chest as he struggled to
maintain his breathing, his eyes never leaving her.

Then he came to her, both of them half-naked,
his eyes surprisingly soft as he looked down into
her face. 'I have never desired a woman so badly,'
he said, but his voice held an almost savage note
to it, as though he was admitting to being fallible,
and that infallibility came much more easily to him.
'Do you believe me when I tell you that?'

It didn't even occur to her to doubt it. 'Yes.'

He dipped his head to one breast, catching one
hard and pointed little tip between his teeth, teasing
and tasting and tantalisingly grazing it, until her
eyes closed and her head fell back, and she felt
herself being sucked into an erotic vortex from
which there could be no escape. She opened her
eyes, suddenly frightened by behaviour which was
so primitive, so out of character for her.

He needed to know that, she decided. And *she*
needed him to know that.

'Constantine,' she said suddenly, and he looked
up.

'What is it, *agape mou*?' From beneath hooded
eyes she could see the opaque glaze of desire.

Her gaze was drawn irresistibly down his body
where she could see the powerful thrust of his
thighs; see too the sheer male strength and power
of his arousal which was pushing insistently against
the fine linen of the trousers he wore. She imagined

him in the act of love, filling her with himself, found herself wondering briefly whether it would hurt, yet knowing that even if it did it would only be the prelude to unimaginable pleasure. She trickled her fingertips over the thick, dark whorls of chest hair, alighting at last on one small male nipple, and she felt him shudder beneath her touch.

'What is it?' he asked harshly.

Jade took a deep breath. He needed to know. 'I've never...' Her voice tailed off, embarrassed.

He stilled instantly, his fingers halting their rhythmic caress of her breasts, his eyes narrowing to charcoal shards. '*What*?' he whispered, his voice dangerously soft.

'I've never—done—well, this...before.'

'You're saying——'

She nodded, swallowing, suddenly regretting that she'd opened her mouth. 'Yes. I'm a virgin, Constantine.'

He swore softly and profanely, and in more than one language, Jade thought, when to her horror and consternation he tore himself away from her and got up from the bed.

'Constantine.' She sat up, the white-blonde hair falling all over her bare breasts, and she heard him say something else, but this time she did not think that he swore; something soft and emphatic and very Greek, before turning his back to her.

'Put something on,' he commanded harshly.

'But——'

'Something to cover yourself. Do it *now*, Jade.'

Her silky T-shirt lay on the courtyard floor. In a confused daze, Jade climbed off the bed and

foraged around in the old chest of drawers before
extracting another T-shirt, not caring what colour
it was or that it was inside out. Weary and sick at
heart, she pulled it on and sat down on the bed.

Constantine had put his shirt back on and was
buttoning it up with inelegant haste.

Jade watched him in bewilderment. Why on earth
was he behaving this way, thrusting her away from
him as if she were a hot potato?

He met her eyes again as he moved to sit beside
her on the bed, putting one arm about her shoulder,
as a doctor would to a patient to whom he was going
to break bad news. He had decided that, for some
reason, he no longer wanted her. OK. Fine. But
Jade just wished he would *go*. Let her be humili-
ated in peace.

With one finger he lifted her chin up, so that she
was imprisoned in the febrile glitter of his eyes.
'Why so sad, *agape mou*?' he queried.

She tried, fruitlessly, to shake the finger away.
'Just go away! Leave me!'

'You want me to?'

'Yes!'

'No. You want to know why I stopped?'

Jade swallowed. 'What makes you think that I
wouldn't have stopped you myself?'

There was the trace of an arrogant smile. 'Because you were ready for me——'

It was the cool assurance that galled her most,
even though she knew that he was being nothing
but honest. 'Why——?' she raised her hand, but he
caught it, pressed the palm to his lips and
kissed it.

'You've been ready for me for days now. You wanted me to take you, to fill you, to make love to you until you cried out. Again and again and again. As you have wanted from the first moment we met. And I would have done that, Jade. Don't you think I don't want that, too? Quite desperately?'

All her insecurities came swimming to the surface. 'Then you don't respect me,' she stated.

'Why not?'

'Because I would have—have——'

'You would have let me?'

'Yes,' she admitted unhappily.

He caught both her hands in his. 'And that is exactly as it should be between a man and a woman. Honesty and passion, no games or pretence—now *that* I respect. But you are leaving tomorrow, Jade. It is not a satisfactory way to begin a relationship and certainly not your first—a night of passion and then a parting. And then I did not imagine for a moment that you would be a virgin.'

That hurt. 'Why ever not?' she demanded.

He shrugged. 'Because English women do not guard their virtue so carefully. And most English women that I have met...' He gave a little movement of his shoulders, as if he was being diplomatic in not completing the sentence.

Jade felt absolutely *furious*. Not only had he shown that he no longer found her attractive, but now he was denigrating English women in general! 'I suppose you've had *hundreds* of English women?' she accused.

'Not at all,' he answered, unperturbed.

'What we don't do,' she said cuttingly, 'is use our virginity as some kind of bartering tool in the marriage market——'

'Enough!' he told her sternly, and caught both her hands in his. She angrily tried to shake her hands free, but he held them too securely.

'No, it is damned well *not* enough! I suppose I should be grateful that you didn't take advantage of me!' she lashed out at him. 'Do you like your women more experienced? Better used to casual sex? Less troublesome to the conscience, I suppose?'

Savagery returned to distort the handsome features into an impenetrable mask. 'Do you think I am that kind of man?' he demanded fiercely, and his accent became more Greek by the second; his presence more dominating. 'One who wants or even needs this one-night stand that you speak of? There is no joy in sex of that nature, and besides that there is something much more fundamental at stake here. You see, *I have fallen in love with you.*'

Jade stared at him wide-eyed, her heart starting to race in exultant beat. 'What did you say?' she said, very quietly.

The black eyes glittered. 'You heard me very well,' he said softly.

She wanted to believe him—oh, how she wanted to believe him. 'But you *can't* love me! You don't even know me!'

'Wrong!' he contradicted arrogantly. 'I knew you the moment I first set eyes on you. As you did me.'

'Oh, Constantine,' she said helplessly, feeling herself beginning to melt. 'I'm lost. Confused. What are you saying? What do you want?'

He moved the powerful shoulders in a tiny shrug. 'I want to spend every moment that I can with you. I want you in my arms when I fall asleep, and beside me when I wake up. I want to make love to you; I think you know how much. But first I intend to marry you.'

CHAPTER THREE

JADE sighed loudly as she settled back into one of the plush leather banquettes which adorned the foyer of the Granchester—undoubtedly one of London's finest hotels.

She had been sent here by Maggie Marchant, her editor—and was waiting to interview Russ Robson for the *Daily View*. Typical! It was just her luck to get stuck with the notoriously lecherous ageing rockstar, but that wasn't the real reason for the deep sigh.

It was because she missed Constantine.

She missed him like *hell*.

Sometimes she could hardly believe that it was only a week since he had stared down into her eyes and said those amazing words which had turned her world upside down: 'First I intend to marry you'.

And she had ecstatically agreed to let him do just that, and as soon as possible—in fact, as soon as he arrived in England, which Jade hoped would be very, *very* soon.

A buzz of excited chatter sounded over by the hotel reception, and she looked up to see Russ Robson approaching.

From a distance the rock-star looked quite good, slim and wearing the ubiquitous uniform of ripped jeans and a black leather jacket. But he was surprisingly small, and as he grew closer Jade could see quite clearly all the signs of a dissipated lifestyle: the bloodshot eyes and the ravaged and pock-marked skin. He swaggered over, and his eyes began a leisurely passage from the tip of Jade's head to her toes as she stood up to meet him.

'C'mon upstairs,' he leered at her as though she were some kind of groupie, 'and I'll give you the interview of a lifetime.' His hand went out to snake around her waist when there was the buzz of some other commotion and Jade looked up to see a group of men walking into the foyer, her mouth falling open in disbelief when she saw who it was, scarcely recognising the evidence of her own eyes.

Constantine.

Jade blinked.

It couldn't be. What on earth would Constantine be doing *here*, and dressed like *that*?

He hadn't seen her; he was deep in discussion with one of the group—another elegantly dressed businessman, who also looked Greek—and she was *sure* that he'd been one of the men seated with Constantine in the taverna, the very first time she'd seen him. She stared again at the impressive and unfamiliar sight he made. The thick and unruly curls had been trimmed and made sleeker, and the darkness of his chin was paler than the smoky growth of stubble which Jade was used to seeing, as though he'd shaved twice already that day.

But it was his outfit which completely knocked the stuffing out of her. He wore a beautifully cut linen suit, but it wasn't rumpled and crumpled like every linen suit *she'd* ever seen—it hung in elegant

folds around the magnificently muscular frame.
Beneath it he had on a shirt of the finest pure white
silk, so fine that she could just make out the
shadowy hint of the thick whorls of hair which grew
in such riotous abandon across his broad chest.
And, with the shirt, a tie of dark green silk. His
shoes were of soft, black leather; hand-made, she'd
bet. He looked ... Jade swallowed. He looked so
different.

He looked ... rich.

Very, very rich.

It was all terribly confusing.

She shook her head a little. His family owned a
restaurant on a small Greek island, for heaven's
sake! He couldn't possibly be *staying* here!

'Hey, babe,' said Russ Robson impatiently, and
Jade recoiled as his arm did actually make contact
with her slender waist, sliding up so that his hor-
rible heavily ringed hand brushed against her breast.

It was at that precise moment that Constantine
looked over and saw her, before she had time to
move, to shake off the revolting Robson's arm, and
what happened next sickened her to the pit of her
stomach.

She saw Constantine stiffen and still, frozen in
beautiful, elegant pose. But there was no welcome
or affection in that hard, bronzed mask of a face.
She watched as his eyes narrowed to become so cold
and so ruthless that Jade felt the icy fingers of pure
fear chill her skin, saw the little tableau they must
make—with Robson's hand resting intimately
around her. She pushed the hand away angrily with
a snort of disgust. Showbiz people were usually

tactile, but Russ Robson had really overstepped the
mark and Jade tried to imagine what Constantine
must be thinking. He must be appalled. He came
from a land where values were much more robust,
more fundamental . . . wasn't that one of the things
that had made her fall in love with the land as well
as the man?

Wordlessly, Jade stepped away from Robson,
automatically moving towards Constantine, scarcely
allowing herself to register that his mouth had
thinned to a hard, cold line, that from his eyes
blazed a stony kind of censure; a look which she
defined all too quickly.

She started to walk towards him, aware of the
murmured comment of one of the men he was with
as she did so. She caught sight of herself in one of
the glittering mirrors, at the blonde disarray of hair
which had fallen out of her French plait to spill in
profusion around her neck. At the two high spots
of colour on her cheeks which seemed to com-
pound a guilt she simply *shouldn't* be feeling. She'd
done nothing wrong.

But you lied to him about your job, prompted
an unnerving little voice inside her head.

'Constantine!' she called, just yards away.

The proud mouth curled. He made a small sound
of disgust beneath his breath before speaking in
rapid Greek to his companion. And then he
walked right past her, as though she was invisible—
no, worse than that, as though she was garbage.
Walked right past her and straight into the lift
without speaking.

CHAPTER FOUR

JADE stood in the centre of the foyer staring after Constantine, watching in disbelief as the lift doors closed behind him, feeling as though she'd just shot herself in the foot.

And then the questions began to crowd into her mind.

Like—just *what* was he doing in the Granchester dressed like that? And what right did he have to walk past her with that haughty look on his face as though she were something the dog had dragged in?

Every right, she admitted to herself gloomily. She had known instinctively that he would have a strongly possessive and jealous streak, and wasn't it part of his charm that he would use passion before logic? Perhaps to Constantine it might have appeared that the pose she struck with Russ Robson was intimate. And what else would she expect him to do while an ageing rock-star gave a display of the wandering hands syndrome? Rush up and ask to be introduced?

'Jade?' Brent, the *Daily View*'s staff photographer, who had been clicking away furiously, was now staring at her curiously. 'Do you know that guy?'

I thought I was going to marry him, thought Jade, which all goes to show that you can never be too old to believe in fairy-tales. 'You could say that,' she answered in a flat tone.

Brent's mouth had dropped open, but she scarcely took in the expression of disbelief on his face. 'How the hell can you——?'

She couldn't face his questions; not when she didn't have any answers which made sense; not even to her. She felt like opening her mouth and howling in disbelieving anger. What was Constantine doing *here*? she wondered in total confusion, feeling so dazed that she automatically sought solace in work. 'I have an interview to do,' she bit out crisply. 'And Mr Robson is waiting——'

'Call me Russ,' came a drawled voice by her side, and she looked up to find him surveying her with curiosity. 'Though perhaps I'm now making sense of those "keep off" vibes you keep sending out.' He jerked his head in the direction of the lift which Constantine had disappeared into, and grinned. 'Rich pickings, huh, baby? But it don't look like he's interested to me. So let's go up to *my* suite, huh?'

Jade's stomach turned over in revulsion. For two pins she felt like telling Mr Russ Robson what he could do with his interview; it was very tempting indeed. But she supposed that would be the height of unprofessionalism, and you didn't just throw in your job at the height of a recession without another to go to. She thought quickly, then gave him a briskly efficient smile.

'It just occurred to me, Mr Robson, that if we do the interview right here in the foyer,' and here Jade gestured to the exquisitely pillared seating area, 'then surely it would get you—er—noticed. And you know what they say about there being no such thing as bad publicity...'

Jade watched as the canny blue eyes considered what she'd said and wondered if he was remembering his last album, which had bombed so badly.

'OK.' He shrugged.

It took the most superhuman effort to put Constantine out of her mind, but an hour later Jade had her interview, in which she had somehow managed to discover that Russ Robson's main passion in life was breeding guppy fish!

'I can think of the headline already! ''From Yuppy to Guppy''!' laughed Brent as he pocketed a used roll of film in the top-pocket of his denim jacket.

But Jade felt sick at heart and couldn't even raise a smile. She found Brent staring at her unresponsive face as if sensing gossip. 'Let's share a cab back to the office,' he suggested, but Jade shook her head.

She couldn't face going back. Not yet. She wanted to be alone with the turmoil of her thoughts. She shook her head. 'Not just now, Brent—I'll catch you later—I've just had an idea for another feature.'

Brent shrugged, looking unconvinced. 'OK,' he said easily. 'See you later.'

At last he was gone and Jade stood hesitantly in the foyer. What should she do now? She needed to talk to Constantine more badly than she had ever needed anything before in her life. But would he agree to see her, and was he actually staying here?

Presumably, as he had taken the lift. Should she enquire at Reception?

Unless . . . and here a cold, clammy sweat broke out on the back of her neck. Unless . . .

What could be the other perfectly legitimate reason for a man taking a lift to one of the hotel bedrooms? What if he was having an assignation with someone? Some beautiful woman lying naked and waiting for him? As willing a capitulation as hers in Greece had almost been . . .

But surely to believe that would be to believe that all Constantine's words to her had been lies. And yet perhaps the most logical explanation was that they *had* been lies. For what was the owner of a restaurant on a small Greek island doing walking around in costly clothes in one of London's best hotels?

But you lied to *him*, prompted the voice of her conscience. Letting him believe that you were some little goody-two-shoes office-worker instead of a tabloid journalist.

Well, she wasn't going to spend the rest of her life wondering what might have happened. I have to *know*, she decided, and, determinedly drawing her shoulders back, she walked over to the reception desk.

'My name is Jade Meredith,' she began.

'Yes, of course, Miss Meredith,' said the receptionist smoothly. 'Mr Sioulas is expecting you.'

Jade's heart hammered, though she couldn't decide whether it was with excitement or sheer fright. 'He is?'

'Certainly. He's in the Garden Suite. I'll get someone to show you the way.'

'Please don't worry,' said Jade hastily. 'I'll find it myself.'

The receptionist made no demur; he was obviously used to the capriciousness of guests. 'Certainly, Miss Meredith. You'll find the Garden Suite on the ninth floor.'

'Thank you.'

The smooth purring of the lift only increased her tension, and when it stopped at the appropriate floor Jade almost turned tail and ran, feeling more frightened than she'd ever done before in her life.

You pathetic little *coward*, she told herself, before stepping forward and rapping loudly on the door.

The door was opened by the man who had been talking to Constantine downstairs. The man she had been sure had been with Constantine in the taverna, thought Jade as she stared into impassive brown eyes.

She forced herself to stay calm. 'I'm Jade Meredith. I believe that Constantine is expecting me.'

A dark head made the faintest inclination, but he offered no introduction of his own. 'Mr Sioulas is inside.' He stepped aside to let Jade pass, and she got the strangest sensation of being summoned into the presence of some ancient potentate, an impression which was only partially dispelled by the sight of Constantine, his back to her, in the most rigid and forbidding of stances, an awesome stillness about him which completely unnerved her.

'Hello, Constantine,' she said, not surprised at the unusually high squeak in her voice.

He stayed unmoving. There was a rustle behind her, and the man who had shown her in rattled off what sounded like a question in Greek.

'*Ochi*!' Constantine's negation was savagely controlled, and the other man withdrew from the suite, one last curious look at Jade as he did so.

There was silence for a moment. This is ridiculous, thought Jade. Is he going to pretend I'm not here?

But he turned around then, and Jade wished that he hadn't, for it was as though the Constantine she had known had gone forever, and in his place was the face of a hard, cold and implacable stranger. She had seen a glimpse of it once, had suspected that it existed, that steely streak—but now she saw it revealed in all its true, formidable strength. And suddenly she knew that only a fool would have believed Constantine to be the owner of a restaurant on a tiny Greek island. This man was no small-time achiever, she realised with a sudden and penetrating flash of insight; here stood a ruthless tycoon.

'Hello, Jade.' But the greeting was denied any warmth by the cutting note of scorn which distorted it. 'To which, I would imagine,' he continued implacably, 'you reply, "Fancy meeting you here!"'

His mimicry, she thought bizarrely, was quite superb considering that it was not done in his native tongue. 'Wh-what are you doing here?' she blurted out, sounding nothing like a journalist and more like a schoolgirl confronting her head teacher with more than a little trepidation.

'What do you think I'm doing here, Jade?' he queried softly. 'Perhaps doing a little trading in the yoghurt or honey which our restaurant produces?'

'Dressed like that?' she blurted out.

He gave a little laugh; Jade had never heard anything more chilling in her entire life. 'Dressed like what, *agape mou*?'

But the term he had once used, she thought, with deep affection now sounded like nothing more then denigration when spoken in a tone which dripped scorn.

How dared he?

'Dressed in clothes which would probably cost a restaurateur's entire year's wages!' she returned. 'The man you allowed me to believe you were!'

He nodded. 'You're correct, you're absolutely correct, Jade. But I think that your accusation is a little misplaced. I did wonder,' he mused, almost as though she were not in the room with him, 'why you agreed marriage to a poor Greek so promptly. Why such a woman would be so willing, so eager to marry such a man—a man so many light-years away from the sophisticates she doubtless deals with in England.' He turned cold, black eyes on her. 'You are wasted in journalism, my dear—you should have turned your hand to acting. Such a fine performance! So convincing!'

It was like some awful dream. So much of what he said confused her, but one thing stood out in her mind: that he had somehow discovered her true identity. In a minute, surely—she would wake up?

'When did you find out that I was a journalist?' she asked quietly, her long fingers pleating at her skirt. 'Did you know on the island?'

He gave her a steady, stony stare. 'On the island?' His mouth twisted into a cruel parody of a smile. 'I think not. If I had known then...' He gave a deliberate pause while his gaze flicked to her breasts, and, hatefully, humiliatingly, she felt them prickle with anticipation; his cold smile indicated that her reaction had not gone unnoticed. 'Then I should not have played the gentleman quite so assiduously.'

The implication was as clear as crystal. 'Then—when?'

He was shrugging out of the linen jacket now, throwing it negligently across the butter-coloured sofa. He walked across to the bar and poured himself a large shot of brandy. He didn't even offer her any, and Jade was suddenly more affronted by this simple lack of courtesy than by any of his earlier insulting remarks; because on Piros he had shown her more courtesy than she had ever received before.

'I'd like a drink, please.' Never in her life had she needed one more.

'Then get it yourself,' he ground out, in a voice of granite.

He watched while she walked over to the cabinet and picked up the heavy decanter with a hand which trembled uncontrollably, and she heard him make a muttered curse in Greek before taking the bottle from her and sloshing some brandy into a second glass.

'Here.' He pushed the glass into her hand, but even that brief contact of skin on skin was electrifying. Jade felt his touch like a whisper of fire to which her body screamed its instant response as if it were bone-dry timber, and she looked up to see his eyes darken, before an expression of disgust marred the autocratic features, and he stepped away from her, swallowing the rest of his brandy in an abrupt gesture of dismissal which spoke volumes.

He walked away from her and began talking softly. 'Let me see, where were we?'

Jade swallowed some of her brandy and the burning liquid to her stomach seemed to revive her. He will not intimidate me, she vowed, wondering why she chose to stay, to lay herself open to the inevitable hurt which would follow, rather than walk right out of that door. But she had to *know*. 'You were about to tell me when you found out that I was a journalist,' she said, amazed her voice should now sound so steady.

'Ah. Yes. When I began to make my plans to join you in England, I thought that as your prospective lover I should surprise you, as lovers often do—to meet you from work with the extravagant bunch of roses. Women appreciate these kind of gestures.'

I'll bet they do, she thought dully.

'But you, Jade, surprisingly, had neglected to give me your work number.' The voice had a steely ring. '*Not* surprisingly, as I now realise. So I rang you at home; late one night. You were not there. Nightclubbing, your flatmate told me. Then I asked her when you'd be back but she didn't know. Very late, most probably. The early hours.' The primitive censure in his voice was stark, the accusation plain, and Jade found herself automatically defending herself.

'There's no need to make me sound like Mata Hari! It's my job!'

His mouth tightened. 'So I believe. Then I asked for your work number—I would ring you first thing. Imagine my astonishment to discover that you work for what can only be loosely described as a newspaper. The kind of newspaper which prints photographs of half-clothed women!'

Which Jade had always hated herself, but she couldn't really imagine convincing Constantine of that. 'How come Sandy didn't tell me any of this? She didn't mention that you'd rung!'

'Because I persuaded her not to,' he said with soft menace. 'I can be very persuasive, you know.'

Jade's mind was buzzing. 'Then today—you being here at the same time as me—you'd—you'd actually *followed* me?'

An expression of scorn mocked her. 'Followed you? After discovering *that*? No, I often stay at the Granchester when I'm in London.' He gave her a black look which could have come from the devil himself before continuing.

'No, Jade, my being here today was purely co-incidence. Coincidence,' he reiterated savagely. 'The weapon of the gods. And that coincidence enabled me to see just how far you would go to get a story with that ridiculous singer downstairs whom you allowed to touch you so freely. But it did not surprise me. After all—you offered yourself to me

without any of the normal persuasion a man has
to use to bed a woman. Was that your brief? Is that
what your editor instructed you to do? To get your
interview with me—come——' and here his voice
twisted with derision '—what may,' he finished
softly.

She had never been so hurt and disgusted in her
life, nor so angry. Too angry to question his absurd
suggestion that she had been sent to Greece to interview *him*, for heaven's sake. Why on earth
should she? A red flare of pure temper erupted and
misted in front of her eyes, and she slammed her
tumbler down on to one of the small tables and
launched herself at him, wanting to punch him, kick
him, scratch him, wound him as he had wounded
her, but he was ready for her. His palms came up
to deflect her flailing hands, then with a swift
movement he had captured both her hands in one
strong hand, holding them high above her head.

She tried to twist, to lock one leg behind his in
classic judo position, but he had countered with
the reverse movement and with his other hand he
held her waist in a vice-like grip, bringing her close
into his body, and she felt his hardness pushing
against her. She stared up in him in horrified disbelief to realise that even after all his vile insults he
still wanted her; wanted her very badly indeed, and
then all thought flew from a mind already punished by the onslaught of emotion as he bent his
head to take her mouth in a savage kiss.

Jade opened her lips to protest as Constantine's
mouth brutally ground into hers but the movement

condemned her for he quickly used his tongue to
sweeten the assault.

Oh, no, she thought desperately, but the half-
hearted struggle she gave only reminded her all too
clearly just how aroused he was, and her body responded like a betraying stranger, so that she gave
a tiny cry, a mixture of anguish and desire as she
felt her breasts becoming heavy, their tips hard and
painful and jutting against the thin silk of his shirt;
and they were so sensitive and aware that through
them she could feel the thick carpet of hair which
roughened his chest.

The pressure on her mouth never ceased, and
something was happening to her; something way
beyond her control. For his hungry, savage need
was matched by her own, overpowering her until
she was nothing but a slave to her own desire. Because she needed him. Needed the man she knew
lay beneath this punishing exterior. She wanted the
real Constantine back, the man she had grown to
love in a few short idyllic days. Surely he couldn't
throw all that promise away—that mutual passion
which happened once in a lifetime, and only then
if you were very lucky? But when his hand moved
down to touch her breast she stopped thinking
altogether—about past or future, right or wrong,
because nothing that felt this good could possibly
be wrong.

It was as though he sensed her mental surrender,
for he gentled the kiss to one of such poignant
sweetness that Jade felt a strange, lingering sense
of triumph, knowing that all could not be lost if
he could kiss her like that. A proud man like

Constantine, who could call a halt on the brink of
rapture as he had done on the island—he would
not be governed by the needs of his body alone.
Dared she hope that he still cared for her? Still loved
her?

She realised that he had freed her hands, that
they had fallen to rest on the broad spread of his
shoulders, and her fingers automatically began
rhythmically to massage at the solid wall of muscle,
loving the warm feel of his strength, longing to
touch his naked skin instead.

He pulled his mouth away from hers. 'Come,'
he commanded, his voice an unsteady, uneven rasp.

She had thought that he would take her into the
bedroom, but he did not; instead he pushed aside
the linen jacket which he had thrown down so
casually, and moved her on to the sofa, which was
scarcely wide enough for them both, forcing him
to lie above her, his eyes staring down at her; hot,
black coals which burned into her heart but told
her nothing.

She stared back at him, her slanting eyes narrowing with confusion, wondering whether she was
doing the most stupid thing imaginable, and yet
rejoicing in the feel of his hard body pressed so
intimately close to hers. Knowing that even if the
hotel were falling down all around them she simply
did not have the power to walk away from this.

He bent his head to hers, and with sweet savagery kissed away her final doubts. She locked her
arms about his neck, her legs parting to receive his
thrusting thigh. She did not know how long he
kissed her for; she sensed his body's impatience,

but none of that was evident in the honeyed seduction of his kiss. She felt an aching pull in the
apex of her thighs, felt her breasts swell until it was
almost too much to bear, and she began to move
restlessly, her senses orchestrating these new movements as though she had been born to do only this.

And only then did he touch her breast again;
little stroking movements, circling round and round
the nipple through her shirt until she thought that
she would die; and precisely as she thought it he
captured the nipple between thumb and forefinger,
rubbing it so that it stood even prouder, aching
desperately to be freed of the confines of
bra and shirt. 'Constantine!' she whispered. 'Oh,
Constantine.'

His fingers never ceased, but he drew his mouth
away from hers to look down at her as he touched
her, his face starkly unfamiliar with passion, a rigid
mask kept only under control by the restraint he
was obviously exercising on his own needs.

'You like it?' He sounded almost casual.

'It's—heaven,' she breathed, but he shook his
head.

'Not heaven. Not yet. Heaven comes later.' He
moved his hand away from her nipple and she made
a little moan of protest, but her mouth softened
into a smile of anticipation as she realised that he
was only doing so in order to unbutton her shirt,
which he did slowly, degree by teasing degree until
her small breasts, encased in a tiny sheer black lace
and silk bra, thrust towards him for his delectation.

She didn't know what caused it, but his face
darkened; his eyes like the blackest recesses of hell

as he stared down at the flimsy, totally inadequate piece of underwear.

'What is it?' she asked him, her question husky, because her lips were swollen and tender from so much kissing.

For answer, he flicked at one nipple in a gesture which was almost casual, though the unsteadiness in his voice belied it. 'Do you always dress to tantalise, *agape mou*?' And then when she made no answer, began to speak again, as if to himself. 'I find myself wanting to rip this foolish little garment from your body. Shall I do that?'

But she didn't want her underwear torn off; not the first time. She wanted his gentleness; his understanding.

'Don't,' she said shakily.

His eyes narrowed as instead he unclipped it at the front, pushing the filmy fragments aside before lowering his head to take one swollen bud into his mouth with the gentleness she had dreamed of, and her head tipped back and she cried out as he made the slowest and most excruciatingly exciting journey from breast to breast, until she realised that she was pushing her hips into his, driven on by some urge she neither knew nor understood.

He moved away then, and she looked up to see that his face was grim as he pulled off his tie and tossed it away. 'Unbutton my shirt,' he ordered softly.

She hesitated, momentarily stricken by doubts, and he watched her from between narrowed eyes before briefly bending his head to suckle at her nipple, and Jade felt a sharp surge of pleasure, her doubts forgotten.

'Do it,' he urged huskily.

With faltering fingers, she started to undo his shirt, stumbling a little as she reached the last button because it was tucked beneath the belt of his trousers.

'Take it off,' he whispered, but she lowered her eyes as she did so. 'So shy, *agape mou*?' he queried mockingly.

For answer, she pulled the shirt off and let it flutter to the floor, and laid her head dreamily against his bare chest, running her cheek up and down it, her fingers losing themselves in the dark whorls of hair, just as they'd done so often in her dreams.

He found the side button of her skirt, and then unzipped it with ease, pulling it down past her knees until he could impatiently toss it aside, and she was left wearing nothing but a tiny pair of black silk panties which matched the flimsy bra.

He said something in Greek then, something very soft which she would have given her heart to understand, and his hand slid down to the soft skin of her inner thigh, teased her there until she moved so that his fingers would touch her where she most needed to be touched, and she heard him give a soft laugh as his fingers moved inside her panties, his hand at last on her moist, heated flesh, and he bent his head to her ear when he heard her helpless moan of pleasure.

'You want me, very much, *agape mou*?'

But Jade couldn't even nod; he was working some kind of magic with his hands, sending her out of her mind, so that she didn't feel like Jade Meredith at that moment, she was being reborn in Constantine's arms and she wondered whether the world would ever be the same place again.

He slid the panties down her legs and threw them off the sofa, while his other hand unbuckled the belt of his trousers, and she heard the zip being drawn down and her heart started beating even more frantically. He moved away to remove the last of his clothing and Jade lay there naked, but not in the least bit shy as she watched the formidable power of him springing free. She'd never seen a man naked before, and yet it felt so right. She allowed her eyes to feast themselves on his magnificent frame, on the massively muscular shaft of his thighs; on the narrow hips and the powerful evidence of his sex. And when he moved on top of her she revelled in the feel of his naked body on hers, of breast touching breast, belly on belly, thigh against thigh. She sighed on a broken little note of wonder.

He kissed her and touched her and she approached some unimaginably beautiful brink time after time, so that by the time he thrust powerfully into her, she was so ready for him, so at one—that there was none of the imagined pain. Indeed, she seemed to know instinctively what to do, entwining her thighs around his bare back so that each thrust went deeper and deeper, and she found herself thrusting back against each movement of his, until she reached the brink once again. But this time it was different; this time he didn't hold back, just kept on moving and moving inside her, harder and harder, until she tumbled over, crying out with wonder and relief as the first great wrenching spasm pulled ecstatically at her womb, and then he too uttered a word which sounded almost like a protest before he shuddered helplessly against her, and she locked her arms around him protectively until she felt him finally still inside her.

There was silence for a moment. His heartbeat sounded muffled and heavy as it gradually slowed down to something approaching normality.

Jade nestled her face luxuriously against his neck, lifting her mouth up to plant a lazy kiss there, when he forestalled her by withdrawing himself from her abruptly, his face averted, before getting up off the sofa.

Aware of the flush which had pinkened her neck and of her nakedness, so noticeable now that he had left her, Jade stared up at him in disbelief. 'Constantine?'

He didn't even look round. 'What?' he asked indifferently.

'Where are you going?'

The unbelievable was happening. He had started to pull on his trousers, and as he zipped them up he turned to look down at her, his face as forbidding as the devil's. 'I'm going to take a shower, then a nap. I don't know about you——' and he gave a lazy, insulting yawn '—but I feel I could sleep for a week.' His eyes glittered. 'But then good sex always makes me feel like that.'

Jade sat up, still not believing what she was hearing, and, seeing his eyes drawn to her still-naked breasts, she grabbed at her blouse in an attempt to cover herself.

His mouth twisted with a cruel kind of satisfaction. 'Oh, don't bother covering up, *agape mou*. I've seen it all, touched it all, *tasted* it all. Here,' and he bent to pick up her discarded clothes and threw them to land in her lap. 'Put your clothes on and get out of here.' And he began to turn away.

Filled with the most bitter, humiliating rage, Jade pulled on her panties and bra and haphazardly buttoned up her blouse, before leaping up to confront him. 'How *dare* you? You lousy——'

But he held one palm up with the calm authority of a policeman stopping traffic. 'Please, no. We've done all that once and once was enough,' he said, in a bored sounding voice. 'Your pretended violence served its purpose—it provoked me into taking you.'

Her anger became something concrete to focus on, because the alternative to anger was tears, and she would sooner die than give him the pleasure of letting him see her cry. She swallowed, but her voice was mercifully steady. 'Let me get this straight, Constantine—you've just been to bed with me, and now you're asking me to leave?'

He shook his head. 'But that's where you're wrong, Jade. On both counts. I haven't taken you to my bed—I've just had sex with you. And I'm not asking you to leave—I'm telling you.' He gave a brief glance at his watch. 'If you get a move on

you might be able to catch the man who was em-
bracing you so fondly in the foyer earlier.'

Jade stared at him. Was he referring to the creepy
Russ Robson putting his arm around her *waist*?
'You can't honestly believe that I'd have...that I'd
go anywhere near Russ Robson after what's just
happened between us?' she demanded hotly.

He gave her a cool, steady stare. 'Can't I?' he
queried softly. 'Who knows what I should believe
about you, Jade? I was even lulled into believing
that you were virtuous——'

Her eyes widened. 'And n-now you're implying
that I'm not——?'

His eyes were cold and unblinking, and Jade was
reminded of the dangerous stillness of a snake.

'No implication. Statement of fact. Might I
suggest that next time you try and convince a man
you're a virgin you try to feign a little innocence.
Virgins don't usually make love with the kind of
panache and fervour which you have just demonstrated.' And he began to turn away again.

Jade tasted salt at the back of her throat. 'You're
sick,' she told him.

'Wrong. I am not sick, merely weary—of you.
Now, are you going to go quietly, or do I have to
ring down and ask Security to remove you?'

It was only by imagining a wax figure of him
harpooned by pins, while pulling the rest of her
clothes on, that Jade could stop herself from
breaking down in front of him. She knew that he
watched her, but she didn't dare look at him. Because if she looked at him she might just rake her
fingernails all down that arrogant face of his.

It was only as she began to open the door that she looked at him, hatred burning from her eyes. 'Oh, Constantine,' she said softly.

The black eyes glittered as he raised his eyebrows in arrogant query. 'What is it?'

'I hope you rot in hell!' she shot, as, back erect, she walked out of his suite and slammed the door shut on his low, mocking laughter.

CHAPTER FIVE

JADE left Park Lane and walked and walked and walked, her body still aching and tingling, her mind in tatters—willing the tears not to come, because she suspected that if she started crying she might never stop. Eventually she found herself back at the offices of the *Daily View*, aware that the other members of staff were staring at her as though she'd just landed in an alien spaceship. And then she caught a sight of herself in one of the mirrors and immediately knew why; she was in shock. White-faced and distraught, she stared numbly while Maggie, the *Daily View*'s female boss, came bustling out of her office and propelled Jade inside.

I'm living my nightmare, thought Jade dully, as she stared in disbelief at the black and white photos which lay scattered all over Maggie's desk.

Photos of Constantine.

Reality became a distant memory. 'Where did you get these?' she asked dully.

'Brent took them surreptitiously. At the Granchester. Honey—do you actually *know* this guy?'

And Jade did the most unprofessional thing in the world and burst into tears.

Maggie dumped a box of tissues in front of her and hurried away to the coffee machine, bringing

back a steaming polystyrene beaker and adding
something to it, before giving it to Jade.

'Here. Drink this.'

Waiting until a shuddering sob had died away,
Jade obeyed, immediately wincing. 'What have you
put in it?'

'Brandy,' said Maggie, who drank a bucket of
the stuff every day. 'Drink it. It'll do you good.'

What it *did* do was increase her sense of being
removed from reality, which Jade wasn't sure was
a good thing at all. Detached. As though what had
just happened had happened to someone else. But
then she felt the aching deep inside her, felt the
tingling of her breasts where he'd bitten and suckled
them, and she knew for sure that it *had* happened
to her. Briefly, she closed her eyes.

She put the empty cup down on the desk and
dabbed at her eyes. 'Just who is he?' she asked in
a quiet voice.

Maggie's eyes widened. 'You mean you don't
know?'

'Of course I don't know—if I knew I wouldn't
be asking!'

'Who did you think he was?'

Jade felt muzzy. 'I met him on holiday. A
gorgeous Greek guy I happened to fall for whose
family run a restaurant.'

Maggie snorted. 'Restaurant! He probably owns
every damned restaurant in the entire Aegean!'

Jade looked up from sniffing into her tissue.
'Who is he?' she repeated.

'He is Constantine Sioulas.'

'I know that.'

'He owns the biggest shipping line in the world. In the millionaire class, he's head and shoulders above the rest. For rich read *billionaire*.'

Jade blinked. 'Ha, ha,' she said, but Maggie's face didn't look as though she was joking. 'He can't do,' she protested. 'He wore jeans; drove the most beaten up old car I've ever seen in my life. He's just an ordinary——' But she bit the word back. No. Not ordinary. No way in the world was Constantine ordinary.

But Maggie had obviously caught her drift. 'He's Greek. They're all like that. No matter what they acquire—and believe me, Constantine Sioulas has acquired more than most—at heart they remain simple men with simple tastes. And simple appetites,' she added knowingly.

Jade was more confused than ever. 'Then why have I never heard of him; why didn't I recognise him?'

'Just because you work on a newspaper, it doesn't mean to say you've heard of every tycoon in the world, particularly one who keeps his head down and his nose clean. You're too young, for a start. Ten years ago when he was twenty, his father died and Constantine inherited—you'd have been about ten at the time, and in my experience ten-year-olds don't read newspapers. The Press went crazy—here you had this young Greek god of a man who was absolutely rolling in it. He stood about a year of it, and then he began to guard his privacy, and the privacy of his family, as if it were Fort Knox. He's always surrounded by at least one minder. He hasn't been interviewed in years.' Maggie chomped on her gum. 'What's he like, Jade?'

Jade's head was spinning. How to describe Constantine? 'He's . . .' What? Gentle? Ruthless? Both of these.

'Good lover?'

Jade nodded without thinking; the brandy was now making her feel as though she'd like to lie down on her bed and sleep for a year. Or a hundred years, until, like Sleeping Beauty, the kiss of Constantine would awaken her.

'And what would you say was the most impressive thing about Constantine?'

As the brandy seeped into her brain, Jade had the sudden overpowering compulsion to confide in her boss. 'His strength,' she said. 'Oh, Maggie—I can't tell you what he was like . . .'

'Try, dear.'

Perhaps if I had a mother who didn't spend her whole time criticising me, I could confide in her, instead of my hard-baked editor, she thought. Somewhere at the back of Jade's mind, a warning bell rang, but there must have been more brandy in the cup than she'd thought, because the warning bell very quickly became indistinct.

'He was so—charismatic. Sexy and strong and gentle and funny. We had a fantastic time. He even—asked me to marry him.'

The unshockable Maggie actually choked on her gum. 'You *are* joking?'

'Why would I joke about something like that?' Although, as each minute passed, the idea did seem more and more bizarre.

'Jade,' Maggie's voice was breathless. 'Are you *quite* sure?'

'Of course I'm sure! How could I be mistaken about something like that?' Jade slammed her cup down on the desk. Her head was spinning and now she felt an unfamiliar lurching feeling in her stomach. 'Maggie,' she mumbled. 'I don't feel very well.'

'I'm ordering you a cab to take you home right this minute.'

'But I haven't filed my piece on Russ Robson.'

'Leave it,' said Maggie uncharacteristically. 'I'll find another piece to fill it.'

Just what that piece was, Jade was to discover the next morning when the demented buzzing of the doorbell bounced into her disturbed dreams about Constantine, and she glanced at the bedside clock to discover that it was almost eight o'clock. And with consciousness, the ghastly events of yesterday re-entered her memory with painful clarity.

The doorbell shrilled yet again.

Pulling her dressing-gown on, Jade stumbled out of bed, looked in the mirror and winced. Who on earth was that at the door? She wasn't expecting anyone, and Sandy, her television director flat-mate, was away filming for a fortnight.

Hope, foolish hope, stirred to life within her. What if it *was* Constantine?

And what if it was? After the way he'd treated her? Now that her mind had cleared from the effects of Maggie's brandy, common sense had prevailed. And if she saw the no-good brute just once more in her life, it would be once too often. If it *was* Constantine, she would tell him to go to the hell he deserved!

But it was not Constantine.

She opened the front door to mayhem. Flash-bulbs exploded in her face as photographers and journalists, some of whom she recognised, jostled on the doorstep like a disturbed ants' nest.

'Miss Meredith—this way!'

'Over here, Jade!'

'Hey, Jade—would you like to comment on the item in this morning's *Daily View*?'

Another flashbulb temporarily blinded her with its lightning-blue flare.

'What's going on?' said Jade, bewildered, then wished she'd never asked, because an early edition of the *Daily View* was held up in front of her nose. She became aware of two things. Constantine's photo.

And hers.

Hers?

And then, she became aware of a third thing; of the headline—shockingly huge and clear and banner-like.

'My Steamy Nights of Love with Greek Tycoon!'

Under *her* byline!

Jade snatched the newspaper. 'Give me that!' She slammed the door in their faces, and, hands shaking like crazy, carried the newspaper into the sitting-room.

It was worse than she could have possibly im-agined. It was a short piece, but to the point. And, apart from the headline, innocuous enough. But it would have repulsed even the strongest stomach with its opening sentence: 'Dewy-eyed cub reporter Jade Meredith described how stunningly handsome Greek billionaire Constantine Sioulas popped the question on an idyllic Greek island...'

Jade dialled the office with trembling fingers and asked to be put through to Maggie, who didn't even have the good grace to sound abashed.

'How could you do this to me, Maggie?'

'It's a good story!'

'But I *trusted* you!'

'The more fool you, Jade.' Maggie gave a shrill laugh. 'You should know by now, dear—once a journalist, always a journalist!'

'He'll sue. He'll sue you for every penny you've got.'

'He *can't* sue!' Maggie's voice was triumphant. 'I checked with our lawyer—and we've printed nothing that wasn't true!'

Jade didn't feel like enlightening Maggie that there had been no nights of love, merely a rather sordid episode in his hotel sitting-room. 'Then I'll sue. I didn't write that.'

'But all of it you said. And I have the tape to prove it.'

Jade listened in appalled silence. 'You *recorded* me?' she whispered.

'Sure. It's my job.' In the background, Jade could hear the sound of someone speaking very quickly. 'Listen, Jade—I have to hang up now.'

Jade sat on the sofa for the rest of the morning, unable to eat or drink or move, feeling like a cornered fox while outside all the reporters bayed for her blood. She shut her eyes in horror. Yes, she'd been angry with Constantine's cold-blooded possession of her yesterday, but not enough to do this. Never to do something like this. She looked down to find that she was still clutching the *Daily View* like a lifeline, and immediately dropped the newspaper on to the carpet as though it were contaminated.

My God, she thought—if Constantine had disliked her before, then his loathing would now know no bounds.

Her reverie was interrupted by the telephone. It was Maggie again.

'Can you get in here right away, Jade?' she said urgently. 'I'm sending a couple of guys down to get you through the Press.'

And Jade did what she had been longing to do for almost a year, uncaring of the consequences. 'No, I can't, Maggie. In fact I'm tendering my resignation. As of now, I no longer work for you.'

There was an odd and somewhat strained quality to the normally robust editor's voice. 'Jade—I advise you to get down here right away. I advise you *very strongly indeed.*'

'Why?'

'I'm not at liberty to say any more on the phone.'

Not at *liberty*? 'Why?' asked Jade acidly. 'Has someone got a gun to your head.'

Maggie gave a strange, humourless laugh. 'Metaphorically speaking, yes. Can I expect you?'

Jade hesitated, her curiosity aroused by Maggie's odd-sounding voice. Was it possible that Constantine *was* going to sue for libel, despite

Maggie's bravado. Oh, how she hoped so. That would show them that they couldn't go around printing whatever they liked about people!

For the first time, Jade knew what it felt like to be on the receiving end of tabloid journalism. But she had never *tricked* anyone into giving her an interview—nor tape-recorded them without knowing.

'Jade?' came Maggie's strained voice. 'Are you still there?'

Jade looked around the room, realising that she couldn't sit in her flat for the rest of her life regretting what had happened, could she? What the hell! 'Yes, Maggie, I'm still here,' she answered coolly. Curiosity got the better of her. 'Send someone over then, and I'll come into the office. But I'm not confronting those vultures outside on my own.' I used to be one of those vultures, she thought. But no longer, thank heavens.

She felt like some minor celebrity when two burly men duly elbowed their way through the waiting Press and into a car, and when she walked through the office the atmosphere was more hushed than usual. At the sight of Jade, all conversation was killed stone-dead.

Head held high, determined that they shouldn't read any trace of emotion in her face, Jade walked towards Maggie Marchant's door, tapped it and opened it to see that it was not the editor who sat behind the cluttered desk.

It was Constantine.

CHAPTER SIX

JADE could only stare in disbelief at Constantine, incongruously seated in her boss's chair. He wore a suit; he looked impossibly elegant and unreachable. And about as friendly as a range of craggy mountains.

His dark eyes flicked over her, and she found herself wishing that she hadn't just thrown on the first items to hand, imagining his lips curling with disdain. But he surprised her. His face remained implacable; not a flicker of emotion whatsoever on the ruthlessly carved features as he took in her short, flared cotton skirt, worn with an old, closely fitting indigo shirt.

He switched his gaze to Maggie Marchant, who Jade now noticed was standing in one corner of the room, uncharacteristically silent and looking terribly out of place. She found herself blinking in surprise—what on earth was happening?

'Leave us,' ordered Constantine.

Jade expected Maggie to reply with a torrent of abusive rhetoric, because no matter how rich and how powerful Constantine might be, in the offices of the *Daily View* Maggie ran a tight ship, with the proprietor giving her an astonishing amount of freedom to run the paper as she saw fit. But no outburst followed; instead Jade was treated to the unbelievable spectacle of Maggie nodding her head and slipping silently out of the office like a messenger-girl.

Little hairs on the back of her neck bristled as she scented danger—the threat of it was emanating from every pore of that impressive frame. She wanted to run and hide from him, from the danger and the ever-present and still powerful attraction she felt towards him. And what a fool you are, Jade Meredith, she thought in abject disgust as she began to turn away.

'And where do you think you're going?' came a silky voice.

She injected steel into her voice. 'As far away from you as possible!'

'Perhaps to sell more details of our so-called affair?' And then the mouth *did* curl. 'I think not.'

A sense of fair play emerged as indignation righteously reared its head. It had been the same while she was at school—it was all very well being punished for something she had done, but not for something she *hadn't* done. But she wasn't going to crawl to him—she would give him the facts coolly and rationally. 'I want you to know I didn't write that story, Constantine!' But to her own ears it sounded blurted and made up. 'Honestly!'

He subjected her to a slow and contemptuous scrutiny. 'If I were you, I would think very carefully about using that particular word,' he suggested icily. 'It doesn't go at all well with your track record.'

'But I *didn't* write it! I wouldn't have had them print it in a million years—I'm just not the kind of person who goes around parading her private life in front of millions!'

He gave a soft, brutal laugh. 'Oh, really?' he mocked. 'Then how did the paper know that I'd been your lover? Or that I'd asked you——' and here he swore very softly and explicitly in Greek, and for the first time Jade was glad she didn't understand the language '—to marry me?' he finished on a note of harsh incredulity, as if questioning his sanity at the time of asking.

Oh, what was the use of trying to explain that she'd been trapped by a combination of her emotional state at being made love to and then dumped by him and the unexpected potency of brandy on an empty stomach? He'd never believe her in a million years, and even if he did, he'd never forgive her, not now. He was not, she recognised— a forgiving kind of man. 'Are you planning to sue?' she asked.

He ignored the question. 'Sit,' he ordered, indicating the chair in front of the desk with a cursory nod of the gleaming jet head.

And because the sheer emotion of seeing him sitting there after everything which had happened between them seemed to have reduced her legs to the consistency of jelly, Jade found herself sinking into the chair.

'Are you going to sue?' she repeated.

He gave an impatient nod of the dark head. 'No, I am not going to sue,' he gritted out tersely. 'There is little point in suing since what was published was the truth—or pretty close to it.' He leaned back in his chair, surveying her from hooded, hostile eyes.

'On a technical point, the article was, of course—inaccurate.' He closed his eyes and recited from memory. ' "My Steamy Nights of Love with Greek Tycoon".'

Jade blushed with shame at the tasteless headline, and he opened his eyes, which narrowed marginally as he took in the heated flares of colour which lay over her high cheekbones.

'As you know,' he ground out, 'there were no *nights* of love; and more fool me. For if I had not been so taken by your convincing little virginal act I would have taken you on the island when you offered yourself so willingly to me. *Over and over again*,' he said in a soft, cruel voice. 'Until I had satiated the aching in my loins, and rid myself of my obsession for you.'

And to Jade's astonishment and horror her body began to react to the brutal sexual boast, and she felt her breasts tingle into life, felt a hot frustrated aching begin at the pit of her belly, and the colour in her face deepened.

His eyes flicked to her breasts, to where she knew without having to look that the pointed outlines of her nipples were pushing against the thin material of her shirt, and his mouth gave another mocking twist.

'And as you know,' he continued relentlessly, 'the physical extent of our relationship lasted a little under an hour——'

Jade got quickly to her feet, her eyes flashing with humiliation and fury. 'I don't have to listen to a minute more of this, you swine!'

'Yes, you do,' he answered icily.

'I'm leaving right *now*!'

'I don't think so.'

Something in the cool and unswervable determination in his voice made her turn around, startled. 'Just try stopping me!' she challenged.

He gave a brief shake of the head. 'I intend to,' he said harshly. 'But not the way you want me to, at least not yet.'

Appalled, her mouth fell open. 'And what's that supposed to mean?'

He shrugged. 'Don't play innocent games, Jade—we've already established that your innocence is a sham. I'm talking about the usual scenario. You run for the door. I follow. You struggle. I kiss you and naturally, you kiss me back. And then I lock the office door, to take you right here. You would like it on the floor, perhaps—or do you prefer the desk?'

The blood thundered in her ears. How could she ever have believed that she cared for a man who could talk to her like this? 'You *arrogant*, unbelievable man——'

'But that's what happened last time.'

No, that's where you're wrong, she thought. Last time, I thought we were both motivated by love; now he had reduced it to the lowest possible common denominator. Lust. Now it was her turn to curve her lips with distaste. 'You disgust me.'

'I know. A pity you find it so exciting.'

She'd had enough. Shoulders back, she made an effort and walked to the door. '*Herete*,' she slung after her, using the Greek word for goodbye.

'I told you, you aren't going anywhere, not until you listen to what I have to say. You have angered me, Jade.'

'Good! You've angered me, too—so maybe we're quits!'

'Never before,' he mused, 'have I been made to look a fool by a woman——'

'Then maybe you should have done! And if you had, it might have made you more human!' she retorted, deliberately putting away the memory of him on the island. He had been human then—delectably human. Powerful yet persuasive, strong and yet gentle. She nudged the thought away. That Constantine did not exist; he had been playacting, too.

'All morning,' he ground out, his eyes dark and gleaming with anger, 'I have had family, colleagues and business acquaintances cabling me to offer their sincere congratulations.'

Jade stared at him in confusion. 'What for?'

Another abrasive laugh. 'On my forthcoming marriage.'

'I'm not with you.' Had he been hiding a fiancée up his sleeve all this time? In which case, he had no right to criticise *her* for supposedly flirting with Russ Robson!

'But yes, unfortunately, you are. You told the newspaper that I had asked you to marry me, and that you had accepted, and with those words I'm afraid that you have sealed your fate.'

Something in the way he spoke unnerved her, and Jade felt a shiver of apprehension trickle its way slowly down her spine. 'What in heaven's name are you talking about? Sealed my fate, indeed! How?'

The black eyes gleamed menacingly. 'I'm talking of marriage, naturally.'

Jade opened her mouth and the word squeaked out. 'Marriage?'

He made an impatient gesture with his hand. 'You will marry me, and as quickly as possible.'

There was a shocked, stunned silence as Jade stared at Constantine in disbelief. He'd flipped! Gone completely mad! She tossed her blonde hair contemptuously back over her shoulders and gave him a chilly smile. 'It may come as a surprise to you to learn that people who despise one another *don't* get married. That's a cute little custom we happen to have in this country!'

'So your answer is no?'

'Of course it's no!' And yet in those oh, so different earlier circumstances her answer had been an ecstatic yes. Unless . . . Her foolish little mind went into overdrive. What if he was genuinely sorry about the way he'd behaved on finding out that she'd lied about her job? Was he now regretting that savage seduction? What if the feelings that he'd had for her, or *claimed* to have had for her on the island, were real? What if he still wanted to marry her for. . .? Her mind dared not even admit the word to itself. But she had to know. 'Why do you want to marry me?'

'Wanting does not come into it. The world now knows that I proposed marriage, which you accepted—and I must honour that commitment.'

Jade's heart did a backward somersault. Of course he wasn't marrying her for love. Had he, since he'd arrived back in England, behaved like a man who was in love? The very opposite. 'I'm not sure that I'm hearing this right. You would marry me simply to honour a commitment?'

His eyes flared like sunlight bouncing off granite. 'Not simply for commitment,' he said harshly. 'For pride!'

'Pride?'

'Yes, pride, or, if you prefer it—honour.'

'I don't understand.'

'That I can believe—but it is a concept which shapes the whole life of a Greek,' he said proudly. 'If I back down now, having given my word that I would marry you—then I will be seen to be dishonourable, and for a man in my position that is something I simply will not countenance.'

Jade went cold at the unfeeling lack of affection behind his words. 'You must be mad,' she whispered, 'to think that I'd ever, *ever* marry you!'

'Don't make me force you, Jade.'

'*Force* me? This is London, you know, not the back of beyond—you can't throw me over the back of your horse and carry me off somewhere!' Even though just the thought of it sent a betraying little *frisson* of excitement through her body.

'More subtle force than that,' he answered, with smooth assurance.

'Oh, really?' She gave a disbelieving laugh, but there was something about the steely determination on his face which again stirred those misgivings into life. 'Like what?'

'Like the fact that two hours ago I bought your proprietor out and that I now own the major controlling interest in this newspaper.'

The room swayed. Jade swallowed. 'You can't have done!' she blustered. 'Not that quickly! This article was only published this morning. You can't possibly have bought the paper!'

'But that is where you are so wrong—with the right financial incentive anything is possible,' he answered, with a cynical smile. 'Surely you knew *that*, Jade?'

She eyed him with frosty disapproval. 'No, I didn't,' she answered witheringly. 'I'm not in the big money league. Besides, whether or not you've bought the paper is of absolutely no interest to me.'

'Oh, I think it is,' he said softly.

He obviously had no inkling of the fact that she was now no longer a member of staff! Jade gave him a superior smile as she savoured her moment of triumph. 'Wrong!' she retorted. 'I've already handed my notice in. So you see—whether or not you own the newspaper has nothing to do with me, because I no longer work here!'

'You wouldn't have done in any case—as my wife I would not have you working on such a scurrilous rag.'

Jade felt like shaking him, if his sheer size hadn't made him so immovable. 'I'm not going to *be* your wife, you ruthless tyrant! Don't you understand? The fact that you own the paper means nothing to me, absolutely *nothing*!'

'Then you care nothing about the fate of your former colleagues?' he enquired silkily.

Actually, no, certainly not Maggie, not after her betrayal, and most of the other journalists would find work on other newspapers.

She chewed anxiously on her bottom lip. Wouldn't they?

'Not particularly,' she said evasively, but her heart sank a little since she knew that several of them were mortgaged up to the hilt. 'Journalists are used to switching around—it's that kind of job.'

'But the others?' he persisted. 'The men in the print room, for example, who I am told by your editor you are rather fond of.' His mouth curled disdainfully. 'But then, they are men, are they not?' The insulting implication was made painfully clear. 'And some of these men,' he continued inexorably, 'look too old to start anew. *If they should lose their jobs*,' he said, with deliberate emphasis.

Jade stared back at him with fascinated loathing. 'You wouldn't,' she whispered. 'You wouldn't do that?'

'Wouldn't I?' he answered remorselessly. 'Believe me when I tell you that I would do whatever it takes.'

Jade often shared a snatched lunch break in the Lamb and Flag with the stalwarts of the print room. She thought of dear old Arthur, saving like mad for his retirement so that he and his wife could retire to a small complex in Spain. And Bill, whose married son was out of work, and whose wage meant that his grandchildren got toys at Christmas. And clothes for the rest of the year.

She stared into the cold, black eyes. 'Are you saying that I could save these people their jobs——'

'If you agree to marry me? Yes.'

This was preposterous—things like this just didn't happen in *her* world! 'You can't,' she protested. 'The unions will——'

'I can,' he said implacably. 'And I will.'

Jade ran her fingers wildly through her mussed hair, closing her eyes as she tried to piece her thoughts together. Could she bear to see people like Arthur and Bill thrown out of a job because of *her* foolishness, *her* indiscretion? And if the only way to put a stop to it was by marrying Constantine...

She looked up into the impenetrable black eyes, and perhaps he read the unwilling capitulation in hers, for the corners of his mouth lifted in an arrogant half-smile of triumph.

'So you'll marry me?' he asked.

'What choice do I have?' she answered bitterly. 'Only someone as heartless as yourself would dream of saying no.'

He made a soft laugh, and rose from behind the desk with all the stealth and grace of a jungle cat moving in for the kill, and Jade eyed him with a deep hatred which was nonetheless mixed with a deep longing which she couldn't seem to shake off. Cornered, she began to back away from him as he approached.

'I want to get a few things straight,' she said, and he immediately halted, eyeing her with a calculating interest. 'You're marrying me *just* to keep your word and maintain your honour?'

'Oh, no,' he negated mockingly. 'Not just for that.'

'It isn't?' Jade's eyes widened as she wondered just what other motivation there could be behind this preposterous marriage.

'No, indeed,' he repeated, on a deep, silky note, which made the little hairs on the back of her neck stand up like soldiers. 'An added incentive is that I desire you with a compulsion which I find profoundly disturbing; it disturbed me when I first met you, and making love to you just once seems to have only exacerbated it. By marrying you, it will enable me to have you whenever I like and how often I like, so that inevitably my desire for you will lessen, and—diminish,' he concluded callously.

Somehow, Jade managed to keep her face poker-straight. 'And then?'

He shrugged. 'Then, in a few months' time—we can divorce, if you wish it.' His mouth became an implacably hard line. 'I will probably have grown tired of you by then.'

'But surely that will heap even more dishonour on your head?' suggested Jade sarcastically.

He shook the black head emphatically. 'Not at all. My family and my Greek friends will doubtlessly expect the marriage to fail from the beginning—and they will blame its failure on the cultural differences between the two races. Besides, if we marry in England in a register office, it won't even be considered a proper marriage, no matter what the law says—because to all my family and friends only a church wedding in Greece will fulfil that function.'

He looked so cold, so hard, as if he were discussing some board-room take over. 'My God,' whispered Jade. 'You've got it all worked out, haven't you? Every single ghastly aspect.'

'But naturally,' he continued inexorably. 'It is the way I always operate. So,' the eyes glittered blackly. 'You agree to my proposal?'

Jade lifted her chin and glared at him. 'I will consider it.' But his attention didn't seem to be on what she was saying, for she saw that he was staring openly at her breasts, and his eyes had darkened into glittering chips of black ice as he began to approach her once more.

She watched as he moved, clasping her hands together to stop them trembling, knowing that she should stray from his relentless path, but something in his face stopped her. Oh, the fascinating planes and shadows of that harsh and ruthless face! It was as though everything which was dark and powerful and savage and masculine—all the primitive qualities which made some men so devastatingly attractive—had been bestowed far too liberally on Constantine. He made every other man she'd ever met seem like insubstantial shadows by comparison.

'And now...' He was so close now: she could smell that soapy fragrance mingled with the hot, salty and aroused male tang of him. 'A kiss for your husband-to-be...' His voice sounded like gravel scraping over velvet.

He lowered his mouth with exacting precision over hers, his tongue gently probing her half-protesting lips apart, and she felt it move slowly into her mouth, sliding erotically over her teeth ... inexorably seductive ... until there was no protest left in her, and she kissed him back. And back ... as the intimacy of the kiss grew and grew. And, with each second that passed, the kiss provoked a tense excitement which built and built and built, so that her body and her heart cried out for joy when he slowly and deliberately swept his hand down over her breast, her belly, briefly alighting on one thigh before encircling her waist.

She felt the hot, fierce and wet release of desire and she gave a little moan, half-crazy with wanting. In the dimmest recesses of her mind some voice of reason spoke its protest, wondering how she could allow him to do this to her after all that had happened.

But the desires of her body seemed to have obliterated everything but its own intense need, and her mind and the voice of reason weren't getting a look in—not when his hand had moved down to unbutton her shirt and she felt the cool air on her skin, immediately closing her eyes with helpless pleasure as he slid his hand inside her bra, so that the exquisitely sensitive nub nudged insistently against his circling palm.

He hadn't stopped kissing her, and his other hand had begun to move her floaty skirt up, and was caressing its way oh, so slowly all the way up her bare and craving thigh, his fingers stroking featherlight touches over the soft skin there. With a muffled groan he pulled her body tightly into his and Jade's eyelids fluttered open as she felt the tantalisingly hard pressure of his arousal which pushed against her, and then, through dazed eyes, saw the familiar yet unexpected sight of her boss's office. Ex-boss, she corrected herself vaguely. Realised, with Constantine's hand almost on her panties, that if she didn't stop him soon, *now*, that he would take her right here, and with as little care or feeling as he had shown before in his hotel-room.

Her mind struggled for ascendancy over body, and with a strength she hadn't known she possessed she pushed him away from her, and stood hastily adjusting her clothing, her eyes dark with rage and passion, her breathing heavy and laboured for exactly the same reasons.

'Don't—don't *ever* do that again!' she declared, once her breathing had steadied enough to allow her to speak. 'Because here's the second of my terms, Constantine. Yes, I'll damned well marry you—because I couldn't bear to see you put those poor men out of work—but it'll be a marriage in name only! And I'm afraid that you're in for a shock if you think you're going to rid yourself of your desire for me by making love to me—because I don't ever want you to touch me like that again!'

His eyes glinted. 'Liar,' he taunted softly. 'Do you really think you could stop me?'

She had the perfect counter-attack. 'You'd force me, do you mean, Constantine? But surely your *pride* wouldn't allow you to take a woman who didn't want you?'

But to her fury, he merely laughed. 'You have an astonishing and enchanting way of showing me how much you don't want me,' he observed arrogantly. 'But don't worry, Jade—you won't have to fight me off.'

Such an about-turn was mighty confusing. 'I w-won't?'

He let out one notch of his belt, as though his trousers were unbearably tight, and Jade found herself having to stare deliberately into empty space so as not to be confronted with the visual evidence of exactly *why* he was having to make the necessary adjustment.

'No, indeed,' he concluded, still in that same, mocking voice. 'You see, living in such close confinement, I'm confident that, whatever your good intentions, you'll find it impossible to stay away from me.'

'Over my dead body!'

'And that if you'll be doing any fighting, Jade, it'll be with your own very healthy desires.'

CHAPTER SEVEN

JADE looked up into the hard black eyes. 'And when do you propose that this—wedding—take place?'

Constantine gave a chillingly ruthless smile. 'As soon as possible. I shall apply for the special licence today. We can be married by Wednesday.'

'And what happens until then—do I go home to my flat to prepare my trousseau?' she asked sarcastically.

'It is not necessary for you to return to your flat.'

'And if I insist?'

He raised his eyebrows mockingly. 'Have you not yet learnt that I will disregard your insistence? Besides, your flat is no longer suitable. Quite apart from its lack of space, you will have already seen how troublesome the Press can be.' His mouth twisted as if with the irony of his words. 'You will come straight with me to my suite at the Granchester.'

Jade shuddered. She couldn't face going back there . . . where . . . She lifted her chin up proudly. 'I'm not staying in that hotel room with you.'

'Why not?'

'Because I . . . Because there's nowhere to——' Oh, why not be honest about it? 'Where would you sleep?' she asked pointedly. 'On the sofa?' Oh, stupid, *stupid*, Jade! Why mention the wretched sofa?

He gave a complacent smile as he homed into her thoughts immediately. 'I doubt it. That particular sofa has far too many erotic memories to be conducive to sleep, is still permeated with your scent...' He let his voice tail off, heavy with suggestion, but then, surprisingly, as if noting her discomfiture at having been reminded of an episode which she would have preferred to remain forgotten, he tried a different tack altogether. 'Do not worry, *agape mou*,' he said, in a gentler voice. 'It has two bedrooms. Propriety will be observed.'

'But what will your family say,' she was unable to resist asking, 'when they discover that you're sharing a suite of rooms with a woman to whom you're not married?'

'You think that this would be the first time it's happened?' he queried softly, and the cruel taunt hit her like a body blow.

Furiously Jade bit her lip and turned away, determined that he wouldn't be able to read such inappropriate jealousy in her eyes.

'Your exposé rather put paid to maintaining any myth that we were prepared to wait until after the wedding,' he drawled. 'But in any case, I am not in the habit of living my life according to the dictates of my family. I answer to no one.'

That, she could well believe. He wasn't a man she could imagine many people standing up to.

Until now, she thought defiantly. And I meant what I said. Yesterday, she had let her passion run away with her, and she'd almost done the same today; but not again. She had learnt her lesson painfully well. He was prepared to take her in as brutal a way as possible, without care and without feeling. She mustn't let him.

'And besides,' he added. 'After I have finished with my business in England, we will be returning to Piros. For our honeymoon,' he concluded softly.

Jade suppressed a shudder. 'Is that really necessary?'

'It is imperative. This wedding will be conducted with all due ceremony.' A strong hand was placed on her forearm, like a gaoler's grip. 'Come. Let us go,' he said. 'The car is waiting.'

Walking side by side, they made their way back out into the outer office, where Maggie was perched on the edge of the sports editor's desk, with the face of a woman who had just gambled away a fortune. Everywhere, fingers stilled on word processors and silence fell like a guillotine.

'One moment, Jade,' said Constantine, and paused, running one hand through his luxuriant hair and looking round at the hushed expectant workers. 'I know that there has been considerable speculation following my take-over. Therefore, I feel it only fair to inform you that there will be no redundancies at present,' he said, and there was an audible murmur of relief. 'And by the way, Maggie,' he remarked, looking around. 'We now operate a policy of no partially clothed women on *any* pages of this newspaper—is that understood?'

'Perfectly,' answered Maggie calmly, as though she had not just been asked to change the entire ethos of the *Daily View*! 'We'll think of something to replace them.'

'Something *suitable*,' murmured Constantine quietly. 'And in keeping with the new goals which I outlined earlier.' Piercing black eyes swivelled in Maggie's direction. 'Perhaps you would like to hold a meeting after we've gone—to outline the turn-around in our editorial policy. Any employee who feels that they would be unable to support such a turnaround will, of course, be free to leave.

'Oh, and by the way,' he remarked, almost casually. 'Miss Meredith is no longer employed by this paper——' He stilled the buzz of comment with the upraised palm of command. 'Because she and I are getting married. Good day, ladies and gentlemen. Come, Jade.'

As exits went, she would probably never better it, thought Jade, a flash of her customary humour returning as she observed the collective opening of mouths before following Constantine to the lift. How she wished she'd had a camera to capture the look on Maggie's face!

'What editorial turnaround?' asked Jade curiously, as they rode down in the lift together.

The back eyes glittered. 'It is quite simple,' he said. 'The *Daily View* is about to change and in future no one will be able to describe it as a "scandal sheet".'

'I see,' said Jade faintly. Well, it would certainly have to change a lot in order to qualify for that!

Outside, a blindingly shiny black Daimler stood parked by the front of the *Daily View* building. There was a chauffeur in the front seat, whom

Constantine introduced as Tony. Beside him was
the Greek man who had opened the door to her at
the Granchester, and Jade found herself blushing
as she wondered whether Constantine had told him
of the outcome of that little meeting.

'This is Stavros,' said Constantine. 'My brother.'

His *brother*? Wait for the animosity, thought
Jade, and then was surprised at the politely formal
greeting.

'How do you do, Miss Meredith?' Stavros ex-
tended his hand. 'I saw you in Piros, but you will
not remember me.'

Jade smiled; he had a kindly face. 'On the contrary,' she said. 'I remember seeing you in the
taverna with your brother. Such a pity we did not
meet.'

Stavros shrugged. 'Indeed. Constantine guarded
you too well. But I am flattered that you noticed
me,' he finished wryly. 'I thought that you and Tino
had eyes only for each other.'

Jade's cheeks went pink. 'I'm pleased to meet
you,' she said politely, if somewhat ironically.

She and Constantine sat in the back of the car,
and he gave instructions in Greek to the driver, but
Jade clearly made out the word 'Granchester'.

'Constantine——'

'What is it, *agape mou*?' he answered softly, and
laid his hand on her forearm, only the lightest of
gestures, but which had her senses on full alert immediately. It was…an almost…well, if not exactly
a loving gesture, then certainly an affectionate one,
and much too close to the way he'd behaved on
Piros for her to derive anything but regret from it.

He's putting on an act in front of his brother, thought Jade, wriggling away from him. He must be. 'What about my things?'

'Things?'

'Yes, things. The kind of things which make such a difference to everyday living! You know—toothbrush, clothes. Little things like that.'

He laughed softly beneath his breath. 'I like it when you answer back, you know, Jade. I find your spitfire retorts *most* entertaining——'

'Well, they aren't supposed to be!'

'And as for your things—we can easily buy you another toothbrush.'

'And my clothes?'

'There is an answer to that which I do not think my brother and chauffeur should be privy to, but if you insist on wearing any then we can arrange to buy you anything you like.'

'But I don't want you to buy me clothes—I happen to have some perfectly decent ones in my own wardrobe.'

His face darkened, with the look of a man obviously not used to having his wishes thwarted. 'I'm talking about garments by the best designers the world has to offer,' he bit out impatiently. 'You can spend what you wish.'

'Keep them! I don't want your money, *or* your designer clothes' answered Jade emphatically. 'I want my own!' Through the glass partition, she was sure that she could see Stavros's shoulders silently shaking.

'As you wish,' he said tightly, and bit out some new instructions, then bent his mouth to her ear.

'So spirited,' he murmured. 'How I shall enjoy subduing that spirit.'

'I shan't let you!'

'We shall see. But I fully intend to.'

And there was no need to ask how he proposed doing that. Jade shivered, the sensual undertones of his murmured words creating vividly erotic pictures in her mind.

Although the car was big, it was none the less claustrophobic and she was intensely aware of his presence beside her. Such a strong and dominating presence. More to keep her mind off his undeniable physical attraction, she asked him a question which had been bugging her since they'd left the building. 'What made you change the policy on the *Daily View*'s pin-ups? Don't you approve of those kind of photographs?'

An expression of distaste masked his face and he crossed one long leg over the other. He stared out of the window at the slow-moving traffic. 'Of course I don't approve!'

Jade shrugged. 'But lots of men do.'

'Not this kind of man, Jade,' he said softly.

'And why do they offend you?' she persisted. 'Do all nudes offend your proprieties, or just some? Do Rubens or Renoir offend you? How about Botticelli's *Venus*, for example?'

He made an impatient sound. 'Nudity in art is different—that embraces and celebrates the female form; these others merely titillate, and of that I do not approve.'

'On purely moral grounds, then?'

He shook his head. 'I concern myself with welfare, too. Those women who pose—they all have mothers, fathers, brothers, sisters—maybe even young children of their own. How do you think that they must feel about it?'

She should have guessed! 'How very paternalistic of you!'

He shrugged. 'And what about you, Jade?' he queried coolly. 'Do you approve of such pictures?'

Jade sighed. 'No, of course I don't approve of them. I absolutely hate them! What woman wouldn't?'

He turned his head to face her, the black eyes piercing and direct. 'And yet you chose to work there?'

'Perhaps it was my only option. Lots of people do jobs they aren't particularly proud of.'

'Is that why you lied to me?' he asked, the timbre of his voice dangerously soft. 'Or do you just enjoy lying for the sake of it?'

Jade met his disapproving stare face on. 'You listen to *me* for a moment, Constantine! All your censure for my having lied about my job, and yet you were guilty of a similar lie. You allowed me to carry on thinking that you were no more than a humble restaurateur. Didn't you?'

'Yes, I'm guilty,' he grated. 'Of being foolish enough to fall for the innocent act you presented to me; foolish enough to believe that you had fallen for the man, and not all the trappings. For me, for the first time in my life, it was a delight to play at being two ordinary people, without all the pressures of wealth. If only——' his mouth twisted

'—you hadn't happened to be a mercenary little bitch who knew *exactly* who I was—who would go to bed with me in order to get the story she wanted.'

Jade felt sick. 'But I *didn't* know who you were, I keep telling you! What do I have to do to make you believe me?'

'Hell will be frozen over before ever I do!' The black eyes narrowed to shards of jet. 'If you hated, as you claim, your job so much—then why do it in the first place?'

'It's a long story.'

'Really?' he queried with an almost polite disbelief. 'I'll bet it is! You must tell it to me some time.'

And she made up her mind to tell him right then because she simply couldn't bear anyone thinking so poorly of her, and it suddenly became tremendously important that he should know that things weren't quite as black and white as he seemed to see them, that she wasn't the hard-hearted villainess of the piece he thought she was. 'I'll tell it to you right now!' she announced, then, exasperated by his disparaging stare, 'But only if you stop glaring at me!'

Their eyes fused in a long gaze, the corner of his mouth tilted upwards by a mere millimetre. 'Very well.' And he leaned forward to close the glass partition between them and the two men in the front.

Jade laced her fingers together in her lap, remembering when she'd thought that the competition had been the answer to all her dreams. Some dreams! 'When I was seventeen and still at school, the *Daily View* ran a competition to find the country's most promising journalist. My teacher persuaded me to enter it, and, to my amazement—I won.'

'Congratulations,' he interjected mockingly.

Jade glowered at the implied criticism. 'Well, actually—I was *proud* of winning, *and* of the article I wrote. When they offered me a job on the staff——' She saw the expression on his face. 'Of *course* I accepted it! Who wouldn't have done?'

'I would have thought about it very carefully.'

'Well, you're a different kettle of fish, aren't you?' she retorted. 'You were rich and I was poor! You probably could have got your father to buy you a damned newspaper—the way you've just bought the *Daily View*! But this was like the answer to all my dreams—I'd imagined starting work on the local paper, so to be offered a job on one of the nationals——'

'But there are other newspapers, surely, more serious newspapers which carry more weight and are more prestigious—why not choose to work on one of those?'

Jade laughed sardonically. 'Oh, come *on*! I was eighteen, green as grass, politically naïve—serious papers don't go for people like that, they want university graduates.'

'And couldn't you have gone to university?'

'No,' Jade answered flatly.

He raised his eyebrows. 'Oh? I find that hard to believe. You certainly aren't stupid.'

'Thanks!'

'So why didn't you go?'

Jade could have shaken him by the shoulders for
his total lack of comprehension as she remembered
her father's strained face, regretfully informing her
that going through college simply wasn't an option
open to her. 'For that very romantic reason of not
having enough money—except that the reality of it
isn't romantic at all! Besides, I thought that
working on the *Daily View* might get me a foot in
the door.'

'But it didn't?'

She shook her head. 'No, it didn't. I didn't—
learn very much there.' She met a pair of frankly
interested black eyes. 'Actually,' she said, remembering some of the *good* things about the *Daily
View*, 'it wasn't *all* bad there. They *do* do some
very creditable investigative journalism. They raise
a hell of a lot of money for charity, and they certainly expose corruption in high places.'

'But that wasn't your particular line?' he queried.

'No,' said Jade bitterly. 'Because I'm a woman,
and a "cub"—I get stuck in features; showbiz. At
first it had novelty appeal, but now it's worn off.
As a matter of fact——'

'Yes?'

'Nothing.'

'Come on—I'm intrigued.'

She met his stare belligerently. 'If you must know,
I came to Piros with the idea of rethinking my
future, and to see whether I had a book in me.'

'And have you?' he asked quietly.

'I don't know yet. I didn't write much for the
first part of the holiday, and then I——'

'Met me?' he finished slowly.

'Yes.'

'I see.'

'And one other thing,' she blurted out. 'My editor happened to *trick* me into talking about you. I was upset and she gave me brandy and kindness and asked me all about you, and all the time she had a tape-recorder going! I certainly did not go to the Press *willingly* about you!'

He muttered something violent beneath his breath, the black eyes boring into her, before looking down to study his hands, so that his expression was shielded from her.

There was a moment's silence. He doesn't care, she thought. Nothing you say will make any difference. She bit her lip, staring sightlessly into the blur of traffic, before returning her attention defiantly to his dark gaze which was now fixed on her face once more. 'Anyway, none of that matters. I don't work there any more, do I?' Or anywhere, for that matter—which didn't bode well for her future once that Constantine had tired of her. She had tried to make her voice deliberately bright but she knew that it sounded put on, and he frowned at her, his lips parting very slightly, and Jade's eyes were drawn to them, and he watched her, his own gaze flickering down to *her* lips. I want him, thought Jade unhappily. How can I stop myself from wanting him? How is it possible to want a man who can treat you so appallingly? Perhaps that's why I've never fallen for anyone before—perhaps I'm a masochist!

An uneasy silence descended and she had to concentrate very hard not to stare at his long legs;

sitting with her own knees held primly closed together, she tried to force herself not to think about him, about the way that he had brought her to that heart-stopping climax yesterday afternoon on the sofa. But it was no good, the memories of it were too intense.

And he could feel it, too—she could sense that from the awkwardly tense way in which he held himself. A brittle stillness enveloped them both as the sexual tension grew. And Jade grew madder and madder with herself. How could she *possibly* still fancy him? The man was a brute!

She could have wept with relief when the car drew up outside her flat. 'Stop right here,' she said coldly. 'This is where I live.'

But, infuriatingly, he followed her inside, pushing his way through the couple of reporters who remained, ignoring all their called pleas for a photo, and slamming the door shut behind them. Once inside, he prowled around, those intelligent dark eyes taking in the simple surroundings—the white walls, the brightly coloured rugs, and, on the wall in pride of place, the water-colour she'd bought on Piros before she'd met him, showing the shaded, narrow streets with the tantalising azure flash of sky which glimmered through one of the arches.

He went to stand beneath it.

'A good choice,' he remarked sagely. 'I know the artist well.'

'I suppose you employ him?' she asked brittly.

'Her,' he corrected brutally. 'And no, I do not.'

Pain, fierce, sharp, unwilling and debilitating— punched at the pit of her stomach. Was the artist who had produced this as exquisite as her painting, with eyes as black as his and hair like the night? Tears threatened to sting the back of her eyes.

'I'll get my things,' she said, and scooted off to the bedroom before she made a fool of herself. Once there, she packed a suitcase full of clothes, hesitating as her gaze halted on the manila envelope on her dressing table. It contained the rough draft of her first chapter. She moved away, then hovered back again, torn with indecision.

If she really *was* going to go through with marrying Constantine, then what was she proposing to do while he went out to work? Surely this was an ideal time to complete the book?

She moved back and picked up the envelope, thrusting it to the bottom of her suitcase, when some sixth sense told her that the bedroom door had opened, and that Constantine had walked silently into the room. She didn't turn round, stayed looking at the suitcase, afraid to look at him, vulnerable in such an intimate setting as her bedroom. 'I'm almost ready.'

'Are you?' he said softly.

He was behind her; she could hear the soft rise and fall of his breathing.

'Please wait outside,' she said shakily, but now she could feel his warm breath on her neck, feel the strong hands at her waist, firmly turning her to face him, and the black ice-fire in his eyes almost blinded her. How could she stay immune to the stark, dark passion so evident in that cruelly handsome face? A passion that he had awakened in *her*; a passion of such strength and intensity that it terrified her.

And excited her beyond belief.

'I'm almost ready,' she said again, foolishly.

'Ready for what?' he queried softly. 'For this?' He bent his head to plant a soft, soft kiss on her neck, and her body was drawn towards his with a trembling yearning.

'Please don't,' she whispered.

'But you want me to. You're ready for me.' One finger trickled with sensitive awareness to find the tip of her breast, and he pressed it with delicate precision, drawing attention to the fact that it was hard and hot and ready for him. Just as he'd said.

'Don't you?' And then he did take her in his arms, but he didn't kiss her, just held her very, very tightly with his arms wrapped around her shoulders, imprisoning her, and Jade had never felt so safe in her whole life. She shut her eyes against his shoulders, recognising one of the truths behind his attraction for her.

That was it; the secret of how he physically overwhelmed her with such ease. It was because the insecurity and chaos of her upbringing had left her feeling rootless, and because she had never met a man like him before. Someone so strong; so sure. Someone you could depend on; lean on.

But she couldn't lean on him, not really. He was motivated to marry her not by an urge to protect her, but through some outmoded concept of 'honour', and a physical ache for her.

That was all.

She should pull away, but the powerful warmth of his embrace held her to him more securely than any chains of metal could have done.

'Let me go,' she whispered weakly against his neck.

'Not yet. I have a much better idea. Let's go to bed. Let me undress you again. God, how I want to do that. It is too long since I've seen you naked, Jade. Just twenty-four hours and yet not a second has gone by when I haven't thought about how it felt to have you naked and helpless beneath me, gasping with delight as I filled you—your body arching as you cried out your climax. Do you know, I didn't sleep at all last night for thinking about it, not at all. It was like a fever,' he whispered in a voice husky with hunger. 'I want to make love to you as with no other woman.'

Jade swallowed; unbearably and shamefully tempted. 'But your brother and chauffeur are outside waiting in the car.'

'Let them wait!' He pulled her closer. 'They can wait all night for all I care.'

She could feel the hard throb between his legs, and oh, she wanted to reach out and touch him there, she wanted to know and explore every gorgeous inch of him. 'But they'll know exactly what we're doing——' Her own voice sounded husky.

'I don't care!' he murmured against her hair. 'I care for nothing other than making love to you——'

She pulled away from him, her green eyes lighting with triumph as she saw the ache of frustration etching lines onto his handsome face. 'But we didn't make love yesterday! Did we, Constantine? We had, as you so charmingly put it, ''good sex'', and do you know, I regret every single minute of it! For two pins I'd like to have the gumption to call your bluff and tell you to get the hell out of here, because I honestly can't imagine that *anyone* would threaten the livelihood of a group of old men by sacking them——'

'Try me,' he taunted softly.

Jade shook her head, saw him watch the blonde hair shimmering in angry tendrils over her shoulders. 'No, I shan't bother. You aren't just anyone—you're ruthless enough to do anything. But let me tell you one thing—we haven't made love and we aren't *going* to make love, either—and if that makes you frustrated, then that's great!'

He gave her a cruel, mocking smile. 'Want to bet?' he queried softly, as his eyes alighted on her strained, pinched complexion. 'I'm not the only one feeling frustrated around here, am I, Jade?'

Ignoring that, Jade drew her shoulders back and continued to berate him. 'And let me tell you something else—that good sex might be enough for you, Constantine, but it certainly isn't enough for me! And now, if you'd like to pick up my suitcase, I really don't want to keep Stavros and your driver waiting any longer!'

And, so saying, her nose held as snootily aloft as she could manage, Jade swept out of the flat.

CHAPTER EIGHT

JADE followed Constantine into the Garden Suite, keeping her eyes deliberately averted from the butter-coloured sofa. Talk about an ever-present reminder of her appalling surrender to his cold-blooded lovemaking; it made her cheeks flame just to think about it! And her heart race with humiliating irregularity.

She glanced down at her bright blue wristwatch. It was now almost five o'clock, and she was as weary as could be.

He loosened his tie and went to pour himself a glass of mineral water. 'Would you like one?'

Jade shook her head. 'No, thank you,' she answered stiffly.

He drank half the water and surveyed her slowly over the rim of his glass, from the tip of her head to her bare feet in their strappy sandals. 'I expect you'll want to freshen up. That's *your* room.' And the dark head was arrogantly nodded in the direction of a closed door. 'Over there.'

Let's hope there's a key to lock it, thought Jade. 'Thank you,' she replied automatically.

'I'll take you for dinner downstairs later. The food is excellent. Be ready at eight.'

It sounded far more tempting than it should have done, but she fought it. She remembered her assertiveness training. Start as you mean to go on.

Maybe if she showed him her notoriously stubborn streak he might think twice about marrying her! 'That won't be necessary,' she said.

'I insist.'

'I'm not hungry.'

'So watch *me* eat.' The white teeth were bared and Jade shivered, reminded of a caged predator she'd once felt sorry for at Chessington Zoo. But *this* predator she didn't feel in the least bit sorry for!

'No, thank you.'

Slivers of ebony glittered with menace. 'So be it,' he said, in a voice so soft that she should have been reassured, and yet needles of ice were scraped with pinpoint accuracy up a spine which was suddenly cold and clammy. 'I'll allow you to play your little games with me, Jade—perhaps you look on it as some form of revenge at being forced into such an ill-conceived marriage to keep me at arm's length, when you know it causes us both nothing but frustration...'

Swine!

'But after the ceremony,' he vowed silkily. 'When you're legally *mine*... don't consider for a moment that I intend to let you play your shrinking virgin act with me—especially when we both know what a farce that particular act is.' He ended the sentence with a look of mocking contempt, but before Jade could even formulate an angry retort Constantine completely took the wind out of her sails by sauntering into his own room and shutting the door behind him, leaving her staring after him, her mouth hanging open like a stranded fish, feeling completely outmanoeuvred.

She went into her bedroom and quickly set about hanging her clothes up in the wardrobe, unable however to stop herself from admiring her surroundings. The room was just lovely, with an unmistakable air of quietly restrained luxury.

After she'd had the longest, most luxurious bath of her life, Jade deliberately stayed in her bedroom, determined to remain there all evening if necessary. She heard Constantine moving around next door, then the sound of the door closing at around eight. Then silence.

She should have been pleased that he'd taken her at her word, had left her alone and gone out to dine, but in reality she was absolutely *seething*! Which infuriated her.

Because why on earth was she wasting her time wondering just who he *was* dining with? What did she care?

Then she started to get very hungry indeed. It was all very well making a point, but Constantine wasn't even around to see her making it! And she hadn't eaten for what seemed like hours.

Jade resisted the temptation to chew on her fingernails. In books the heroines always seemed to go for days without food, so why couldn't *she* be like that? Any minute now, if she didn't get something in the way of sustenance, she might just be tempted to start gnawing at the hearth rug!

She picked up the telephone.

'Yes, madam?'

'Er—is it possible to order something to eat?'

'Certainly, madam.' Did the voice sound amused, or was she just getting paranoid? 'Mr Sioulas said that you'd probably be feeling hungry.'

Swine!

But after a steak sandwich and the most expensive half-bottle of claret on the menu Jade felt a good deal better, good enough to find herself whistling a little tune as she hurled herself under the duvet, wearing her best pair of black cami-knickers, and the flimsy little top which accompanied it— just dying for the opportunity of fighting Constantine off when he came in from dinner.

Her next recollection was waking up at mid-morning and throwing on a matching black satin wrap to wander mid-yawn into the drawing-room, her hand raking back through the tousled blonde disarray of her hair to find Constantine, fully and immaculately dressed, as though he was going to an appointment in the city.

And Jade couldn't help the powerful pang which wrenched at her heart at the sudden and utterly devastating sight of him first thing in the morning.

The olive face was impassive, the black eyes secretive, but there was no mistaking the flash of hunger which lit them as they alighted on her semi-clothed state. 'Good morning. You slept well, I trust?'

Was that a twitch of amusement she saw at the corners of his mouth? She found herself wanting to demand what time he'd come in, why he hadn't come in to... oh, for heaven's sake, was she *mad*?

'Very well, thank you.'

'I've rung for some coffee.' He glanced at his watch. 'I'm afraid that I shan't be able to join you, as I have a meeting to attend.'

Jade shrugged, feigning nonchalance, trying to convince herself that if he *had* joined her she'd be eager for him to be away. He was just using subtle psychology, that was all, probably following that old adage—what was it they said? 'Treat them mean, and keep them keen'. Well, he was in for a shock if he thought she was going to fall for that one!

He left minutes later, and Jade was left to fill up her day. In the event she had a wonderful day. All the time she'd lived in London and she'd never even been to St Paul's Cathedral, Westminster Abbey, the Tower...so she set off sightseeing with a vengeance.

But when she arrived back in the suite at just after four o'clock it was to find Constantine waiting for her, pacing the floor like an expectant father and resembling a caged panther even more strongly. As the door closed behind her, she saw the two big hands clench beside the muscular shafts of his thighs, the knuckles white, as though it were only through the most supreme effort that he didn't physically manhandle her.

'Where the hell have you *been*?' he demanded, before she'd barely closed the door behind her.

Jade knew enough about people to know when they had reached the end of their tether. 'Sightseeing,' she answered, frowning.

'*Sightseeing*?' He made it sound as though it warranted a gaol sentence. Black eyebrows knitted together in two formidable dark slashes. 'How?'

'Well, first you buy your ticket, and then you——'

'Silence!' he bellowed. 'I mean—how did you get there?'

Jade stared back in confusion. 'Well, by Tube, of course!'

He swore long and profoundly in his native tongue; incomprehensible to Jade, but it wasn't difficult to get his drift. 'You little fool!' he ground out in English, just in case she'd missed the message.

Jade looked up at him, her green eyes troubled. He sounded seriously worried. 'What have I done?' she asked in confusion—had she forgotten to pull the door shut? Had the suite been burgled while she'd been out?

He shook his head impatiently. 'Do you not realise that, as my fiancée, you are now the target for all kinds of lunatics?'

'What,' she ventured, 'exactly are you talking about?'

'I am talking about *kidnap*!' he emphasised harshly, then nodded grimly as he saw her wide-eyed look. 'Yes. It happens. Your clothes were here, and you were... I thought...' His face blackened with a terrifying rage again. 'In future you will use the car and the driver I have provided for you. Do you understand?'

She'd never seen a man so angry before; he was almost shaking with it. It was frightening to see someone who she had imagined to have an un-breakable control, to be that close to losing it completely. And he was intelligent enough for his fears to have some rational explanation to them, rather than just the nebulous fears of the over-cautious. Jade found a wave of sympathy washing over her as she registered the sharply defined lines which divided the very rich from the ordinary person. A life haunted by the threat of abduction. She might resent him for forcing her into marriage, yes, but not enough to send him over the edge.

'I should have left a note,' she said quietly. 'I won't do that again.' Then, to divert him, 'Shall we have some tea—I'm absolutely parched?'

He stared at her for a long, long moment, and then some spark fired at the depths of the coal-black eyes, something very like reluctant humour lifted one corner of his mouth.

'Tea?' he echoed faintly.

With equal reluctance, Jade smiled back. She could get quite used to seeing him look ever so slightly nonplussed, she thought. 'Yes, tea,' she reiterated. 'And if you spare me your "you English and your tea", speech, then I won't tell you that Greek coffee has the consistency of mud!'

He laughed then. 'But that's not true, is it, Jade? As I recall, you *loved* Greek coffee——'

She quickly turned away to pretend to look out of the window, afraid to speak, shaken with a strange, debilitating sadness and precariously close to tears at the intimate sound of that simple little memory. It was also, she realised, the first time she'd heard him laugh since the magical time they'd

spent together on the island, when he hadn't seemed
to stop laughing. In fact, he had marvelled about
it at the time—that she had the ability to make him
laugh, almost . . . as though that in itself were a rare
commodity.

'I'll go and freshen up,' she said hastily, grateful
that he said nothing, but aware of his watchful eyes
on her retreating back.

When Jade went back out into the sitting-room,
the tray of tea had arrived, and Constantine was
stretched out in one of the armchairs, his eyes
closed. His long legs were elegantly sprawled in
front of him and there were lines of fatigue etched
deep on the craggy features. Just for that one brief
moment she was reminded of her own father; a
million years away from Constantine in lifestyle
perhaps, but looking similarly exhausted as he
battled to earn the kind of money which would
support the spending habits of his extravagant wife.
A battle he had finally lost.

Silent though she was, the moment her foot went
down on the soft carpet Constantine's eyes flickered
open immediately, and Jade's senses prickled as she
was caught up in the compelling blackness of his
gaze.

'You look tired,' she said, without thinking.

His eyebrows were raised fractionally as if surprised by her solicitude. 'Yes. Your tea should
revive me.'

'For what?'

His hand moved to rub wearily at the back of
his neck. 'I have a business dinner.'

He said it with a quiet acceptance which caused her to look at him with new eyes. Suddenly she saw through to the loneliness and isolation of the tycoon, the omnipotent head of a vast organisation. Maybe there'd never been anyone in his life to tell him to slow down. She tried to dampen down another rush of definitely unwarranted sympathy. 'Do you *have* to go out on business tonight?'

'Why?' The voice was mocking, and the black eyes flickered over her watchfully. 'Are you offering me a more attractive alternative?'

Jade didn't react as she sat down in front of the tea-tray. 'I merely meant that you look as though you could do with a good night's sleep.'

'But I'm not going to get one, am I?' he queried silkily. 'Not when I know that you're right next door to me.'

'But you slept OK last night,' she pointed out.

'Did I?' he parried. 'Are you quite sure about that?'

'Tea?' asked Jade, a fixed smile upon her face as she picked up the heavy silver teapot, thinking rather hysterically that she sounded like one of the characters from a comic farce.

'Thanks.' He took the cup that she offered him, adding a wafer-thin slice of lemon, and for a while the scrumptious contents of the tray were enough to take her mind off their sleeping arrangements. Jade bent her golden head over the various plates as she busily examined and began selecting contents from the assortment of dishes on the tray.

'Mmm!' she murmured enthusiastically, slightly embarrassed when she looked up into a pair of bemused black eyes. 'I haven't had a cream tea for years!' she found herself explaining lamely.

'Haven't you?' He smiled. 'Me neither. Cholesterol be damned! Pass me one of those scones, please.'

In the end, it proved a surprisingly companionable meal as they both ladled thick home-made strawberry jam on to the fluffy scones, and compounded the damage by adding big spoonfuls of clotted cream.

Jade was absolutely starving and Constantine seemed amused by her delicate greed. 'Good?'

It was terribly easy to like him when he was in this kind of benign, indulgent mood, she thought. He'd been like that when she'd first met him and now, as then, she found it impossible not to return his rare smile. 'Mmm,' she murmured with satisfaction, as she leaned back in the armchair and stretched her arms above her head. 'That was delicious—I feel absolutely full.'

But with an abrupt movement he put his cup down on to the table. 'There are a number of things we must discuss.' His voice seemed to have assumed its habitually gritty quality, and their earlier mood of something resembling camaraderie was immediately broken.

Jade sat upright and took a sip of her tea. 'Such as?'

'Who you wish to come to our wedding.'

'You mean I have a choice?'

The black eyes flashed a silent warning. 'I mean that I have no intention of letting your ex-colleagues provide a "scoop"—but that if you wish your parents to come, then obviously——'

'No,' cut in Jade quickly.

His eyes narrowed. 'You're quite sure?'

On the island they had not, she realised, done more than merely skate over their family life—he knew that she was an only child, and she knew that he had a brother and a stepsister. Her own reluctance to talk about it had been due to the highly unsatisfactory nature of her early years. Now, for the first time she began to wonder whether his own reluctance stemmed from a similar source.

'You don't wish for either of your parents to come?' he asked curiously.

'No.'

He frowned. 'I see.'

He didn't, not really. Jade realised that her bald answer must sound uncaring. Not that it could possibly matter if he thought her an unfeeling daughter. He couldn't possibly think any worse of her than he already did. But even so, she decided to elaborate, for her pride's sake more than any need to confide in him. 'My father is dead——'

'I'm sorry,' he said quietly, and a totally new expression came into his face.

She rushed on, not wanting to be affected by the sympathy which had softened the dark eyes. 'My mother is on her own—she lives in Devon. Her health is—frail. The journey would be too much for her.'

'Even if I arrange for a private jet?'

Jade swallowed. Even if he arranged for the reception to take place in the presence of the Queen, it would make no difference. 'Thank you, but no.' She saw the puzzlement darkening his eyes, and suddenly she wanted the score evened—why had he never talked about his own family? 'And your family?' she challenged. 'Will they be attending?'

'No,' he said determinedly. 'Just Stavros, as witness.'

'I see.' She put her cup and saucer down, under-standing immediately his own reasons for not wanting a family celebration. Because why bother when the wedding was nothing but a farce? To have his family come dance at it would make further mockery of it. And yet, didn't it hurt more than a little bit to imagine a cold little signing of papers in some anonymous little register office some-where, when she'd once imagined an enchanting union with them whispering their heartfelt vows to each other?

Jade rose to her feet, feeling drained, and knowing that her face was blanched of all colour. 'If that will be all,' she said, in the manner of a secretary speaking to her boss, rather than that of a prospective bride speaking to her husband-to-be. 'Then I'll go to my room.'

He inclined his dark head, but said nothing, and Jade, with the prospect of another long, empty evening ahead of her, found herself wishing that he had asked her to join him tonight, at his business dinner.

She would have said no, of course, but it would be nice to have been asked.

CHAPTER NINE

JADE, refusing to cower in her bedroom as though she'd done something wrong, was sitting in one of the armchairs watching the television—though she couldn't have described a single second of the programme she had been watching—when Constantine emerged from his room, ready for dinner. He had showered and changed and was wearing the most exquisitely cut suit in deepest blue, and a dark blue and white spotted tie of raw silk knotted around the strong sinews of his neck. The dark wavy hair was almost dry, but a tendril had fallen on to the wide and aristocratic forehead, and this one untidy deviation in an otherwise immaculate appearance somehow added even more to his physical appeal. As if he needed anything to do that, thought Jade ruefully.

He stood looking down at her for an instant, the lean face indifferent, but not as cold as before. 'Get some sleep,' he instructed. 'There are dark shadows beneath your eyes. Goodnight, Jade.'

She watched as the door closed quietly behind him and found herself again wishing that he *had* asked her to have dinner with him. But what would have been the point? Too many cosy get-togethers like the one they had shared this afternoon over tea would surely be detrimental? That way spelt danger, and the threat of her succumbing to the subtle web

of charm he could spin. And painted a false picture
of him. Because the way he'd behaved while sharing
scones with her was about as far removed as it was
possible to be from the man who had ruthlessly
seduced her, then taken over the newspaper and
threatened to boot out half the staff if she didn't
agree to his proposal of marriage.

Jade continued to try and concentrate on the
documentary before giving up; and, going into her
bedroom, she had a quick shower, then changed
into an Edwardian nightgown of fine lawn,
brushing her newly washed hair and leaving it
hanging loose all the way down her back. She read
a book, rang down for a salade Niçoise and a glass
of milk, and after she'd eaten and brushed her teeth
she took the book to bed with her to read.

It was a story which a few weeks ago she would
have thoroughly lost herself in, but tonight the
words on the pages bobbed around like midges, and
eventually she gave up the struggle and turned out
the light.

She thought she'd crash out as soon as her head
hit the pillow, but sleep was surprisingly slow in
coming. Behind closed eyes, she kept seeing
Constantine's face in its many guises—stark with
passion, dark with a fiercely controlled rage,
exhausted and weary, and—this afternoon—like a
rare jewel, the sight of his uninhibited laughter
again. Pathetic really, to think how much that had
warmed her in response.

Sleep came, but it was the deep yet restless sleep
which accompanied a troubled mind. Jade found
herself far away from the comfort of her luxury

hotel bed, poised instead in the doorway of an empty house, her panama school-hat on her head, the sunlight streaming in from the bright day behind her, even though the house was strangely dark. And cold.

'Mummy?' she called out tentatively into the silence. 'Mummy?' But the silence continued, growing more vast and more awesome by the second as she realised the implication of the sealed letter addressed to her father which lay on the hall table. '*No!*' she screamed. '*No!*'

'Jade!'

The deep voice penetrated her consciousness. Warm, strong hands were on her shoulders, shaking her awake.

'No!' she screamed again, and then fell into the blissful safety of an embrace, but a masculine embrace, not her mother's embrace. Her mother had never embraced her...

'Sssh.' His voice was strangely comforting, but it seemed to come from a long way away. 'Sssh. It's a dream, *agape mou*,' he murmured into her hair. 'Nothing but a dream.'

But if this was a dream, then she never wanted to wake up. Here, half awake in his arms, existed a kinder reality, an infinitely more attractive reality than the true circumstances of why they were together. In dreams, wishes could come true...

She didn't want to open her eyes; she wanted her dream to stay, never wanted to leave it. She allowed his arms to tighten around her, knowing that she had found what she wanted. She wanted this:

Constantine's   protection   and   Constantine's
possession.

But he was breaking into the tender and blissful
disorientation she felt at being within the strong
circle of his arms. Breaking in with a question she
didn't want to even acknowledge, for to do that
would be to resurrect the unbearable pain of her
childhood.

'Jade,' he whispered softly. 'What is it that
troubles you? Is it the marriage?'

The marriage? Right at this moment, with her
emotions swamping her senses, marriage to him
seemed like a bedrock of heavenly security. If only
the rock didn't happen to be built on sand...

'Is it the marriage?' he asked again, and she
shook her head, her silky hair fanning over that
warm, strong neck as she did so, and she heard him
sigh.

'What, then?'

She shook her head.

'*Tell* me,' he urged her. 'I can help.'

Who could resist such a soft appeal from such a
normally steely man? Certainly not Jade, half
asleep, and half... half in love with the man... 'It
was just a dream. I'm being silly——'

'Let me be the judge of that. Something made
you dream badly. What was it?'

It came out in a rush then, like a bottle of cham-
pagne which had been shaken vigorously. 'When
we talked earlier——'

'About the wedding?'

'Yes, but not that.'

'What then?' he urged, his voice deep and husky.

Jade submitted to its command. 'It was—when we were talking about my mother...' Her voice tailed off, ashamed, helpless.

'*Tell* me! I need to know.'

With her eyes still closed, she could picture it as though it were yesterday—the clarity of the unwelcome memory had not diminished over the years. 'I don't know what made me mention it. I was ten and my parents had taken me on holiday to Brighton. My mother went——' Jade's voice faltered. 'Out. It was pouring with rain, and the hotel was tiny. My father took me to a café for lunch. I think the waitress felt sorry for us, because she let us stay, and we sat there all afternoon, playing I-spy and watching the rain run down the windows.' Snake-like rivulets. Like tears. 'Then we went back,' she finished flatly.

'And your mother was waiting for you?' he asked curiously.

'That time, yes.' Her mother's voice had been slurred from too many cocktails at lunchtime, her cracked voice shrilling insults at her bewildered father. It had been their last family holiday; Jade had not known it at the time, but the cracks had been starting to widen irreparably even then.

'And the next time?' he prompted discerningly.

That soft, dark voice could coax blood from a stone, thought Jade as she found herself nestling further into the beating warmth of his chest. 'One day—oh, it must have been a year later—she didn't come back. She'd—she'd—met another man.' The

passing of the years hadn't dulled the pain of
memory. 'I came home from school one day to find
that she'd—gone. I didn't see her for years, not
until after my father died last year. I rarely see her
now, and even now the relationship is . . . rocky . . .'

'I'm not surprised!' Constantine's eyes narrowed in disbelief. 'She *left* you? She left her child?'

'Is that so inconceivable to you?'

His voice sounded savage. 'Of course it is. The
bond between mother and child is unbreakable.'

'Then you're very lucky, Constantine. That your
mother wouldn't have dreamed of leaving you.'

He shook his head. 'Not in the way you speak
of, no. She died when I was twelve.'

She opened her eyes immediately, struck to the
very core by some indefinable note in his voice. It
was the first time she had ever seen any trace of
vulnerability in the severe lines of his face. No
wonder he never talked of his family. 'I'm so sorry,'
she whispered. 'I didn't mean to——'

He briefly laid a finger over his lips, shook his
head. 'I know that.'

But his voice held no recrimination and the
darkness gave her the courage to question him
further. 'And your father?' she ventured.

In the shadowy half-light, she saw the faint
outline of that hard mouth twist, though whether
it was with pain or derision she couldn't guess. 'It
broke him,' he said simply. 'It was a love match,
you see. But he . . .' There was a pause.

'He?' she whispered.

Now there was definitely derision there. 'He
married again a year later.'

Jade let out a sigh. 'Why?'

'Because he felt that Stavros and I needed a mother—especially Stavros, who was so young. As if *anyone* could have taken her place,' he said bitterly. 'Instead he found himself a wife and a stepdaughter whose sole purpose in life seemed to be the elimination of his fortune.'

She said nothing; nothing *to* say—but for answer she let her lips drift upwards to kiss his cheek, very very gently, and she heard him softly expel the air from his lungs.

'Now——' And he moved his hands purposefully to her shoulders, as if to distance her, but she couldn't bear to leave the safe haven of his embrace, here, where childhood scars were eased and soothed. And so she nestled closer into his chest, pushed her cheek against the strong column of his neck, his scent invading her nostrils and overwhelming her with its distinctive masculine aroma.

She felt his heart quicken beneath her breast, felt his arms imperceptibly tighten around her shoulders, and still he said nothing, just started to stroke her hair with a rhythmic caress which had her sighing with pleasure.

'Go back to sleep,' he urged her quietly.

She said nothing in response to this, but she felt her body answering for her—in the thrust of her nipples which had begun to nudge insistently against that hair-roughened chest, in the hot ache between her thighs and in her hungry lips which lay passively against his neck, but in whose centre beat an eager pulse which longed for his kiss above all else.

She heard him mutter something beneath his breath, felt him shift a little as if to move away from her. 'I must go,' he said with quiet emphasis.

But Jade did not want to be alone with her fears and her insecurities and her nightmares. More than that, she did not want him to go. Not tonight. Tonight she needed Constantine, as she needed no other. She laid her soul bare for him to see, and in doing so she felt completely empty. She needed Constantine to cover her, to fill her, to make her whole once more.

'Don't leave me,' she whispered.

'I must.'

She gave a tiny shake of her head. 'Stay.'

There was a sense of urgency in the deep voice. 'But if I stay, you know what will happen?'

'Yes.'

'Better another night.' She could hear his reluctance, but in her need, she chose to disregard it. 'When you aren't so...' He paused, as if searching for a gentle put-down.

He was giving her a way out, but she didn't want to take it. 'When I'm not so—what?' she whispered throatily. 'You told me you wanted my body; told me you wanted to slake your desire until it was no more.' Her eyes fluttered open to surprise a look of such naked, feral heat which burned in the depths of his eyes, but she began to tremble. 'Are you telling me now that you weren't speaking the truth?'

It was as though her own tremor had set up an answering response in his, for she felt a shudder rake through the length of his body.

'Were you?' she whispered. 'Speaking the truth?'

'You know I was,' he ground out. 'But then I spoke in anger. Tonight there is no anger between us; tonight...' His words tailed off.

'Tonight?' she prompted, in a husky whisper.

She caught the gleam of steel from behind the narrowed eyes. 'You are vulnerable tonight, *agape mou*. And your heart is aching——'

'Then take that aching away,' she said softly, astounded by her own daring, but urged on by needs which could not be constrained by the mere convention that the man should be the seducer, and not the woman.

There was a pause; she could almost hear him battling with his conscience—if a conscience he had.

But how could he have a conscience which was troubling him now, after he had taken her so cold-bloodedly and without compunction the other day?

Could it be because she knew and he knew that if he came to her tonight it would not just be 'good sex' as he had so ruthlessly said after that frantic coupling on the sofa just next door? Tonight, her emotions were too raw and exposed; she had laid herself open to him honestly, as he had to her, and she knew, with some kind of unerring instinct, that tonight he would have to respond to her in kind. With his heart.

If he came to her. She closed her eyes, prepared for him to take his leave of her.

'Open your eyes,' he commanded. 'And look at me.'

Weakly, she obeyed, fearful of what she would read in his, but she saw his own need shining through the dark waters of that ebony stare.

For a long moment, he stared down at her, and then, slowly, lingeringly, began to kiss her mouth as if he had all the time in the world.

It was a kiss so delectably sweet that she started to tremble again; she had never believed that a kiss could be so poignant and so tender. The last time she had lain in his arms like this, he had kissed her with all the masculine authority of the dominant sex, had branded her with fiery kisses which led straight into the blaze of sexual consummation. But this kiss—it was infinitely more subtle; and in its way far more distracting. She felt her eyelids flutter to a close again.

'No!' came the soft command, the accent very slightly emphasised. 'Watch me now, as I watch you. Drink in my body, Jade, as I do yours, and see the effect you're having on me. Keep your eyes open all the time, and watch me while I love you.'

Her gaze ran hungrily over him. He was still wearing the suit he'd had on earlier, and as if he'd captured her thoughts he gave a small, brief smile before momentarily releasing her to shrug out of the jacket where it fell to the floor with a whisper. He sat, motionless on the edge of the bed, his eyes fixed firmly on hers, compelling, waiting.

With trembling fingers she reached out to unknot the silk of his tie then to pull it off and discard it, so that it joined the jacket on the floor. Suddenly shy, she made as if to move her hand away, but he stopped her with a shake of his head.

'Continue,' he murmured. 'I like it.'

Jade swallowed as she slowly unbuttoned the shirt, until it revealed the olive-skinned torso, shadowed by the hair which grew there. He took the palm of her hand, laid it flatly over his heart, and she heard the dull thundering of his heart which hammered out his desire for her.

He took the shirt off, then pushed her gently back against the pillows before turning his attention to the fine white cotton of her nightgown. It was full of detail; she'd bought it for just that reason—tiny tucks and pleats, and a myriad minute pearl buttons, which he began to snap open, one by one.

'So English,' he murmured. 'So very, very English.' He peeled the nightgown over her head and threw it aside, staring down at her, his eyes blazing as he drank in her nakedness. She shut her eyes hurriedly; afraid to look into his eyes for fear of what she might read there.

'Open them,' he commanded again. 'There is no need for shyness.' His hand slipped to his belt, which he unbuckled with unhurried ease, so that he somehow managed to instil infinite grace into the act of stripping off the rest of his clothes, until he was as naked as she and he climbed into the bed and pulled the sheet over both of them.

For a moment he lay above her, his desire pressing hard and full against the softness of her belly, and she breathed a sigh of delectable anticipation, her mouth curving into a soft smile of pleasure. His eyes narrowed momentarily with some unknown question as he stared down at her, and Jade knew the briefest surge of uneasiness, but it was dispelled as his arms went about her, their bodies moulding even closer and their lips fusing in a heady union which threatened to stop her heart.

CHAPTER TEN

IT WAS the most perfect night of her life, and one which Jade would remember for the rest of her life, no matter what happened between them afterwards.

Her instincts had been right; it had not been 'good sex'—it had been much, much more than that. Constantine had made love to her over and over again, she had lost count of the times she cried out her pleasure into the silence of the night, but when she awoke in the morning he was gone.

As if he'd never been there; not one scrap of clothing remaining to show that he'd spent the night in her arms. Nothing to show, but plenty to feel. And not just the aching deep inside her, or the tiny bruises of teeth-marks on her swollen breasts—the discovery that he was no longer there beside her produced both anger and pain. She recognised bitterly that on the two occasions he'd made love to her he'd cast her off afterwards with a ruthlessness which left her feeling nothing short of cheap.

And why not? What did she expect? Nothing had changed. He still believed that she had deliberately deceived him, had tried to seduce him into getting a story. He still believed she had kissed and told by giving her story to the *Daily View*.

What she didn't understand was why he had been so reluctant to make love to her last night, after boasting to her that he intended to talk his way into her bed.

And why she had been so reluctant to let him go back to his own room, after everything *she'd* said. Was it just that the man was capable of throwing all her senses into overdrive, or did it go deeper than that? Was she still, as she suspected—still in love with him?

Damn Constantine Sioulas, thought Jade, as she pulled on a bathrobe and padded through into the shower.

Half an hour later, she had just finished brushing her hair when there was a knock at the door. It was Stavros.

He gave her what appeared to be a genuine smile, which she returned, hoping against hope that she didn't resemble a woman who'd just spent the night being ravished by his brute of a brother. How many of those had Stavros seen over the years? she wondered. *I don't want to be just like all the others*, she thought, with a pang of regret for her *stupid*, impetuous behaviour—pleading with him to stay the night with her while knowing that there could only be one outcome if he did. And didn't men— particularly proud and possessive Greek men like Constantine—only respect women who fought them off? She sighed. What a mess everything was.

'Hello, Stavros.' She was *not* going to ask. Was she?

'Er—do you happen to know where Constantine went?'

Shaking his head, Stavros gave a broad grin and a wink as if to say that her question as to his brother's whereabouts was entirely predictable. 'He didn't tell me—but he sure as hell looked *mad* when I saw him first thing.'

Her heart sank.

He narrowed his eyes—eyes like splinters of jet, so like Constantine's own, and yet lacking something of their enigmatic brilliance. 'Did you two have a fight or something?' he mused.

Not unless the dictionary version of fighting had undergone a radical change overnight. 'Um—not exactly.'

Stavros shook his head. 'What is it that you do to him, Jade? He's been like a crazy man since he met you, you know?'

'Yes,' answered Jade drily. Crazy was right. Sane men did not generally blackmail women they considered had wronged them into marrying them as some primitive form of revenge!

Stavros gave her a quick look. 'I know he's not always easy,' he began.

Jade almost laughed. 'You're certainly given to understatement!'

Stavros shook his head. 'He hasn't always had it easy himself, you know. People think that the money is an answer to everything, but it isn't.'

She knew that. She remembered his fear that she'd been kidnapped, his apparent isolation as he'd sat fatigued in his chair yesterday evening. But that wasn't really relevant to *their* situation.

But Stavros seemed to be possessed of a great need to present Constantine in a more favourable light. 'You know that our mother died?'

'Yes, he told me.' Her voice softened. 'You were very young?'

'She died giving birth to me,' said Stavros, and her heart went out to him as she heard the emptiness and confusion in his voice. 'I don't think my father ever got over it, really—even when he re-married—no, *especially* when he remarried. So Tino became like father and mother to me. He was only twelve.' He hesitated, the hero-worship there for her to hear as plain as day itself. 'Don't make the mistake, will you, Jade, of thinking that the harsh exterior you see is all there is?'

Jade said nothing, just stared at Stavros sadly. If only he knew. He was romantically, foolishly labouring under the misapprehension that she and Constantine were marrying for love. *She* might be in love, she realised with a sinking resignation but *he* certainly wasn't.

Stavros cut into her thoughts. 'What time do you want to leave?'

'Leave?' she echoed in confusion.

'Sure. He's left the car and the driver at your disposal.'

'What for?' Jade blinked, then remembered how he'd flipped because she'd trailed around London on her own yesterday, on the Tube. Perhaps he meant that she should play the tourist again.

And then another thought occurred to her, a thought which, surprisingly, she found infinitely more disturbing. What if Constantine had come to his senses after their night spent together—wouldn't that explain his hurried departure? Perhaps now that he'd had a night of passion with her he had slaked the lust he felt for her, and had decided to call the whole thing off. And perhaps the car was there to take her home to her flat, and out of his life forever.

Stavros cleared his throat. 'He said you should go and choose your wedding-gown. It's tomorrow, isn't it?'

Bang went her theory, and, infuriatingly, her heart accelerated! 'Oh, did he?'

'Mmm. You don't sound overjoyed.' Stavros eyed her speculatively. 'What's the matter? He's a good catch, my brother. Don't you know how many women have wanted to marry him?'

'I can imagine,' answered Jade acidly, then, seeing Stavros's almost hurt look of bemusement, she relented—it wasn't *his* fault that his brother was such a ruthless swine, after all!

Stavros frowned. 'You know that he hasn't invited our stepmother or her daughter?' He paused, and a fleeting narrow-eyed look crossed his face, making him look uncannily like his big brother.

Jade nodded. 'He told me.'

'Do you know why?'

Yes, she knew. Because they were just going through the motions of a wedding, that's all—so why make it a farce by inviting all his relatives?

Stavros frowned. 'Marina—that's our stepmother—she won't particularly care one way or the other, but Eleni, that's her daughter—she's going to go absolutely *crazy*. She thinks the world of Tino.' He stared at Jade. 'Can't you make him invite her?'

'I don't think I can, Stavros.' She didn't imagine that it was possible to make Constantine do anything which he didn't want to.

Yet it seemed that he still wanted the wedding to go ahead, even if it was going to be a small and rather hushed-up affair, and if that was the case then she needed a dress to wear. A woman had her pride, after all!

So Jade spent the day being ferried round different shops in the low, sleek car—watching people peer into the interior whenever it stopped at traffic lights, obviously hoping to see someone famous. Sorry to disappoint you, she thought wryly, as she leant back against the soft, luxurious leather. She really could get used to this kind of life, she decided regretfully, remembering her own rainswept waits at bus-stops.

In the end she bought a cream linen dress with a matching hat, which looked stunning without breaking the bank, since she determinedly refused every one of Constantine's charge cards which Stavros tried to press into her hand.

'Take them,' he insisted.

'I don't want them.'

Stavros shook his head mournfully. 'He'll be mad.'

Good! 'That's not my problem,' she shrugged.

'Maybe that's what he likes about you—that you make him so mad!'

If only he knew, mused Jade as she walked back through the revolving doors of the Granchester, purchases in hand.

Constantine was in their suite, and to Jade's quickly stifled dismay she noted that his face was unwelcoming and tense as she appeared in the doorway. She didn't know what she had expected after she had given herself to him so passionately last night, but it was certainly not this cold and intimidating face he presented. He gave her a brief, terse nod, but that was it. No smile, no kiss, no embrace, nothing to let on how close she thought they'd been during the night. But perhaps that closeness had all been in her naïve and fevered imagination. She was relatively innocent; he was not. The kind of rapturous response which she'd demonstrated as he'd made such superb love to her was probably par for the course where he was concerned. How many women had sobbed out their pleasure in his arms and had their tears wiped away with his supposedly tender kisses? she wondered painfully.

'I have the licence,' he announced dispassionately. 'We marry tomorrow.'

Jade vowed to match his icy politeness. 'The sooner it's done, the sooner this farce of a marriage can be finished.'

A fleeting look of anger distorted his features, making his eyes as black as ink. 'The days, perhaps. But not the nights,' he taunted softly. 'Do you not want those to go on forever? Or did my ears deceive me last night when you begged me not to stop?'

Jade's cheeks flushed hotly. What a louse he was, to bring that up in broad daylight. She met his gaze full on. 'I was overwrought last night, not surprisingly. But it's a mistake which I shan't make again,' she vowed fervently. Even if it killed her.

'No?' A mocking smile twisted his mouth. 'Forgive me if I find that somehow hard to believe, Jade. You're hungry for me all the time. Even now, while you profess to hate me so much.' And his eyes dipped insultingly to her breasts, which tingled and throbbed under his blatantly sexual scrutiny, and she turned away from him, horrified by the betraying response of her body.

'So do I take it you won't be joining me for dinner tonight?' he asked silkily.

'Correct!' she rapped out.

'Beauty sleep before we take our vows? I guess you need it.'

The implication was brutally clear—she certainly hadn't got very much sleep last night. Oh, *what* had possessed her? Why did the night play such cruel, deceptive tricks? Last night he had seemed like security personified, solid as a rock in the dark loneliness of her nightmare, comforting her and loving her with his body. While now he was a cold-faced stranger who eyed her with nothing but lust, making mockery of the binding intimacy she had imagined they'd shared. 'I'm going to my room,' she said icily, and turned her back on him, but halted at the curt command of his next words.

'The wedding takes place at ten. We leave here at a quarter to the hour.'

Jade hesitated, wondering just what agenda he was proposing for their wedding-night. 'And after-wards?' she asked, as coolly as she could.

'Afterwards we travel to Piros.'

*   *   *

The blistering heat hit Jade like a sledgehammer,
and she was so exhausted that she allowed
Constantine's hand to support her back. His black
eyes remained impenetrable and his mouth was a
tense, thin line as he helped her out of the small
rowing boat which had brought them from his
luxury yacht, now moored just off the island of
Piros. Seeing the island where they'd been so happy
sent shock-waves of regret through her, but she determinedly kept her face poker-straight as she stared
at the contrast of the deep lapis lazuli of the sea
lapping against the white sand.

They had spent the last twelve hours travelling,
flying from Heathrow to Athens after the wedding,
then being driven to Piraeus Harbour to board the
yacht.

'Tired?' he asked softly, his eyes narrowed as he
watched her gaze flicker round to where people sat
drinking and eating in the tiny quayside tavernas.
Hard to believe that a few short weeks ago the two
of them had roamed the island, hand-in-hand and
carefree.

Jade nodded, swallowing to try to dispel the
stupid lump in her throat. The journey *had* been
long, and tiring, but it was the emotional strain of
her whole wedding-day which had left her feeling
as weak as a kitten.

However much of a farce the ceremony might
have been, she had still found it unbearably painful
to go through the motions of the simple wedding
service. To have to say 'I will' to Constantine, and
then to have him slip the ring on to her finger, and
act like it meant nothing to her, when quite clearly

it did. But the worse had been to come. After the registrar had pronounced them husband and wife he had pulled her into his arms and told her that she looked exquisite, before kissing her thoroughly in front of the registrar and a grinning Stavros and Tony so that she was left quite dizzy and breathless.

Because it had all been a front—that much was obvious since for the rest of the journey he had lapsed into a terse and moody silence, punctuated only by curt enquiries as to whether she wanted food, drink, another cushion, to sleep or to read. 'Just let me know if there is anything that you want,' he had said eventually, in the same hard, cold voice.

She knew exactly what she wanted. She wanted all this to be real. She wanted, not politeness, not even passion. She wanted love.

And now they were on Piros she knew neither for how long, nor for what purpose.

She held her head stiffly, unaccustomed to the heavy style of French plait, still dressed with the fragrant white flowers which Constantine had insisted on ordering for their wedding. 'And how long do you anticipate we'll be staying?'

He stared out at the dark blue band of the horizon. 'That depends,' he answered obscurely.

'On?'

'A number of factors, but I do not intend to discuss them here. You are tired, Jade. I will take you to my home.'

My home, she observed. Very territorial.

Before she knew it he was strapping her into the same beaten-up old jalopy as he'd driven her around

in when she'd met him. In view of what she now
knew of his lifestyle, his choice of car seemed decidedly incongruous. 'Why do you drive this, when
in London you have a limousine?' she asked
curiously.

He changed gear with a smoothness which was
amazing, considering that the car seemed to be on
its last legs. 'That's city life,' he shrugged. 'The
world I move in expects symbols which demonstrate status and wealth. So I play the game. But
I'm not turned on by cars.'

'As long as they get you from A to B?'

He shrugged. 'You have it in one.'

'This one might take longer getting from A to B
than most!'

He laughed. 'Sure. But this car's very special to
me.'

The dusty silver-green of the fragrant cypresses
began to appear and Jade wound the window down
to sniff their evocatively warm scent. 'Why?' she
asked, as she looked at the doorknob which hung
on only by a prayer.

He drummed long, olive fingers on the steering-
wheel. 'I won it.'

'How?'

He gave a wry smile. 'In a fight, I am ashamed
to admit.'

'Different!' murmured Jade, but her interest was
alive. He didn't, she realised, give away much of
his past. 'Who did you win it from?'

There was a pause. She thought that either he
hadn't heard her, or that he wasn't going to reply.

But then he did.

'It's a long story.'

'I like stories. Car journeys are designed for story-telling.'

At this he grinned, which he didn't do very often. And when he grinned he was thoroughly irresistible.

'I grew up and was educated in Athens,' he began. 'But I used to come to this island every summer—even after my father died. He grew up on an island like this, you see, and he wanted me to know something of the life he'd had. A simple life. But I was the city boy; the rich boy—always the outsider.' He swerved to avoid a rock, muttering something in Greek, and Jade was afraid that he would clam up just when she felt sure that she was about to get some insight into what really made him tick.

'Don't stop,' she said quickly.

He gave her a brief, sideways stare. 'There was one boy in particular—his name was Kris.'

Kris. Somewhere in the back of her mind, the name rang a bell.

'Kris always took particular exception to my being here. His dislike grew worse over the years. He fancied himself with the ladies and——' He made a little shrugging movement with his shoulders as his voice tailed away, and Jade didn't have to be told what one of the problems must have been. Even if the boy had been an Adonis, he wouldn't have got a look-in with the ladies with Constantine around.

'And he was the leader of the other boys,' he continued. 'He used to challenge me to fight him and, when that wouldn't work, to goad me into fighting him.'

'But you wouldn't?'

'I don't fight for fun.'

Jade shivered, in spite of the violent heat of the day. 'What happened?'

'One day, he went too far. He picked on a boy younger than himself.'

'And you——?' prompted Jade, with horrified fascination, thinking that this was the stuff that adventure films were made of.

'I taught him a lesson. He'd just bought a car. We fought for it.'

'And you won, right?'

He shrugged; smiled. 'Naturally.'

'But why d'you keep it?'

His face went suddenly tense. 'Because, for a long time it was the hardest thing I'd ever had to fight for...' His voice tailed off on a strange note as he glanced across at her, then back to the road.

Jade swallowed. 'But was he—all right?'

He actually laughed. 'Not for a week or so, but yes, he was all right—what did you think I'd do—kill him?'

'I wouldn't put anything past you, Constantine!' she said with feeling, then turned to study his strong profile. 'So that was the end of a beautiful friendship, was it?'

He grinned. 'For a while. Then, years later, he came to apologise to me, and to seek my help.'

'Your help?'

'He wanted to set up a restaurant.'

'And you helped him?' she asked incredulously.

'Sure. It was a good business proposition. And it's better in life to have a friend than an enemy. As a matter of fact,' he said coolly, 'you've eaten there. Often.'

'I have?'

'Sure. Remember that first night when I took you out for dinner——'

As if she wouldn't remember every second of it for the rest of her life. She saw the proud tilt of his jaw and recalled what he'd said at the time. 'The owner owes me a favour'. Kris! Of course! He'd waited on them. Good grief!

The car had been ascending the hilly interior, and Jade could see the bright glitter of a large white building which clung to one of the hills like a child to its mother's hips. She remembered the way their eyes had met over the head of the child in the taverna. Something preordained had happened at that moment. She had fallen hopelessly in love with him, however crazy that might seem. And suddenly she knew that, whatever else happened between them, her fate had been decided for her in that one long, shared look. She knew with a chilling certainty that her love for him would simply never go away, for it was part of her now, as much a part of her as her limbs.

Doomed, she thought gloomily. To love a man who is going to use our brief marriage to try to rid himself of his desire for me. 'Is that where we're going?' she asked, pointing up at the house.

'It is.' His voice was mocking. 'You wanted a honeymoon, didn't you?'

'Not particularly!'

'Liar!' he taunted softly.

She wore nothing but a short, sleeveless lemon dress, and she became quickly aware that the pinkening flush to her skin which accompanied just the *thought* of a honeymoon was easily visible all over her neck and shoulders, as well as on her face.

'I rest my case,' he added, with cruel observation.

Did *nothing* escape him? 'Well, if you're expecting to consummate this so-called farce of a marriage, you'll have a very long wait!' She turned to him, her voice quiet but determined.

'Bravo!' he applauded. 'Brave words, Jade! Fighting words! And empty words!'

'We'll see,' she challenged fiercely, although she knew that her argument was seriously flawed, because he was right, she *did* want him—incessantly. But she was not going to...not again. To have a wild and passionate night of bliss and the next day for him to behave in that cold and contemptuous way, as if the night had been nothing. And because he could not have even the most scant regard for her if he considered that sex was her motivating force. How amused her ruthless blackmailer would be if he discovered that it was love...

The car drove off the main road and on to a small track, then bumped up to the white building over which the rich velvet hue of a magenta bougainvillaea bloomed royally.

Despite her inner conflict, Jade couldn't stop herself from drinking in her surroundings with pleasure as she stepped out of the car, but Constantine's attention was elsewhere, and she heard a terse exclamation as she saw him stride to the side of the building, where another vehicle was parked beneath the shade of a lemon tree.

A car which couldn't be more different from the beaten-up one which Constantine had driven here.

It was a large and long, gleaming silver Mercedes. Jade shuddered to think of the cost of bringing such a car to such a small island.

'Who's here?' she asked him.

'We have guests,' he bit out, in a voice which could have sliced through metal quiet easily.

At that moment there was a flurry of sound, and the front door was flung open and a woman, who Jade judged to be in her late twenties, stood on the shadowed step. She possessed the proud patrician features and the strong dark colouring which immediately marked her out as Greek. There was a small silence before she stepped from out of the shadows into the full glory of the brilliant sunlight which bounced in a blue-black dazzle off her gleaming hair.

She was simply beautiful, thought Jade with a sudden sinking of her heart, and she was dressed in a spotless cream silk dress and coiffured to perfection. But then she looked into the woman's face and almost started with shock at the message revealed there. Her dark, almond-shaped eyes glittered with undisguised hostility as she stared directly into Jade's face.

'Surprise!' she called, with a husky Greek inflexion, and started to move towards them, her arms held out in greeting, pointed scarlet nails like talons outstretched. 'Welcome home, Constantine!'

CHAPTER ELEVEN

THERE was a moment's silence before Constantine stepped forward, a polite smile on his face as the beautiful brunette caught his hands and they exchanged a kiss on each cheek.

Constantine turned to Jade. 'Jade, darling,' he said smoothly, and Jade almost started at his use of the unfamiliar endearment in English. 'You must let me introduce you to Eleni—my sister.'

'Oh, Constantine,' chided Eleni, batting superb black lashes which didn't need one scrap of mascara to emphasise them. 'There isn't a drop of shared blood between us. I'm your *step*sister. Remember?' The coldness re-entered her brown eyes as they flickered from Constantine's face to Jade.

'So *this* is your bride,' she said haughtily, and there was a theatrical pause. 'Not at *all* what I would have expected. Hello, Jade,' she gushed insincerely.

And I can be just as insincere, thought Jade as she pinned a bright smile onto her lips. 'Hello, I'm very pleased to meet you,' she said, holding out her hand and receiving a limp imitation of a handshake in return.

Eleni's head was perched to one side, like a watchful bird. 'You're so very *young*,' she observed.

'Twenty,' Jade defended, her misgivings growing by the second. There were all kinds of strange undercurrents going on here, she could sense them as easily as if they'd been visible to the naked eye. She could see an alertness and a rigidity about Constantine's stance, could sense the blatant sexual challenge which glittered at him from Eleni's eyes. *She wants him*, thought Jade, with a sudden sick feeling. What the hell had he brought her to?

He fired a question at Eleni in Greek, which only increased Jade's sense of being an outsider, and Eleni replied in the same language, giving Jade a smug stare as she did so, as though sensing her discomfiture.

Constantine turned to Jade, his voice softer. To sweeten the blow, she wondered fleetingly?

'My stepmother is inside. Come, we shall go and meet her.'

Eleni turned to Jade. 'We're *very* cross with Constantine for denying us the pleasure of attending his wedding. When I rang Stavros and he told me it was taking place yesterday—I couldn't believe it——'

'Damn Stavros!' swore Constantine succinctly. 'He was under strict instructions to tell no one.'

Eleni hooded her eyes with their heavy lids and slanted him a look. 'But for heaven's sake, why, Constantine?' she queried, mischief sparking her exquisite features. 'We've waited for so long for you to plight your troth, and then you rush away and do it in secret. Almost——' She gave a malicious smile. 'Almost as though you were ashamed of your beautiful young bride.'

Jade flushed, wishing that she could spirit herself away from here by thought alone. What the hell was Constantine playing at?

'Unless, of course,' said Eleni maliciously, 'there's some *other* reason for the indecent haste?' And she looked pointedly at Jade's flat stomach.

Jade flushed. 'There's none,' she said smoothly, thinking that if Constantine didn't get her away from this woman in a moment, she wouldn't be responsible for her actions!

As if he'd homed in on her thoughts, he caught her elbow. 'Come,' he said softly.

The inside of the house was deliciously cool and dark. Jade got a brief impression of marble floors, of white walls and shuttered windows, before Constantine took her into what was obviously the formal drawing-room to meet Eleni's mother.

And if she'd been hoping for some dear little apple-cheeked old lady, she was in for a shock, because on first impression the pencil-thin beauty who sat on a high-backed chair looked little older than Eleni herself.

On first impression.

Closer to, Jade could see the ravages of time, made far more apparent by the older woman's determination not to give in to them. Thick foundation lay in the deep lines which tracked over her face, cruelly emphasising them, and the bright blue which glistened on the heavy eyelids—so like

Eleni's—were like a throwback to the sixties, as were the thick black false eyelashes.

'Marina,' said Constantine. 'May I present to you my wife, Jade?'

Jade was subjected to another chilling scrutiny as she took the gnarled old hand in hers. Marina inclined her head briefly, then spoke in rapid Greek to Constantine, who shook his head.

'We will not, I think, speak in any language other than English since Jade is not yet familiar with Greek.'

'*Yet*?' mocked Eleni. 'And you plan to actually *learn* our language, do you, Jade?' she queried disbelievingly. 'Believe me, the English find it almost impossible.'

Some devil sparked insubordination in Jade's soul at the put-downs which the two women were loosely handing out. This marriage might be a farce as far as Constantine was concerned, but if he was playing the part of contented spouse, then she could go one better. And if it infuriated Eleni that she had married Constantine—then she would *really* give her something to get her teeth into! She gave a smile. 'I realise that, and I certainly don't underestimate how difficult it's going to be, but I'm quite determined, aren't I, Constantine? Especially if you teach me. He's the most *wonderful* teacher,' she confided glowingly. 'In just about everything!'

The black eyes glittered briefly at her in response before he turned back to his stepmother, a look of polite query on his face. 'This is most—unexpected,' he said carefully. 'To have company on our honeymoon.'

Eleni smiled without humour. 'You must allow us women our little foibles. We have brought Sophie with us to prepare a small wedding feast—but do not be troubled, Constantine—we are intent on leaving in the morning. And surely your bride will allow us one meal with you?'

Constantine gave a small nod of his head. 'You are, of course, most welcome to stay with us for as long as you like, and naturally Jade and I are honoured and delighted to share in a surprise meal with you. Have you——' and his black eyes looked as hard and as forbidding as metal '—planned to invite any others for this—er—feast?'

'Just the four of us,' said Eleni, a cool smile playing on her lips. 'Which will give us the chance to get to know each other better. Now please, Jade—sit. You stand like a stranger in your husband's house. Sit and Sophie will bring us refreshments—you must be parched after your long journey.'

'Thank you.' Jade sat down on the edge of one of the overstuffed chairs, her knees pressed tightly together, feeling a bit like a child invited to the party, who nobody had really wished to come.

Eleni picked up a small silver bell and rang it, and on cue a small, rather harassed-looking woman scurried in, her face lighting up with unconcealed joy as she sighted the tall form of Constantine who stood with his back to the window.

He strode over to embrace her, indulgently
listening to her excited torrent of Greek, and then
he turned and said Jade's name, and something else,
very slowly in Greek, so that the woman beamed
as she took Jade's hand.

'*Kalispera sas*,' said Jade, as her hand was
grasped tightly. '*Pos issaste*?' And was rewarded
for this extremely elemental greeting by a squeal of
delight from Sophie, and a small, amused smile
from Constantine, and it shook her how his ap-
proval could hearten her so.

There was stilted small talk until Sophie re-
appeared bearing a tray of coffee and four glasses
of iced water. Eleni lifted up her stately blue-black
head. 'It's Greek coffee, Jade,' she murmured. 'But
I know that a lot of foreigners find it unpalatable.
If you'd prefer it I can easily order some regular
coffee for you?'

Jade swallowed as her smile remained in place.
'Thank you, but that won't be necessary—I happen
to adore Greek coffee.' And she saw Constantine
smile at her as she accepted one of the tiny cups
with alacrity.

Constantine remained standing, and his immense height seemed to dominate the room. His
eyes had flickered to Eleni's hand. 'You no longer
wear your ring, Eleni? Your hand seems much
smaller with the absence of such a magnificent
diamond.'

Eleni shrugged narrow and elegant shoulders, her
red-tipped fingernails fluttering as she spoke. 'I am
no longer engaged,' she told him, her dark eyes

slanting at him with some unspoken message as she
did so.

Constantine's hand paused, the cup raised
midway to his mouth. 'Oh?'

'She broke it off,' said Marina, a tight look of
disapproval about her heavily red-glossed mouth.

Constantine's face hardened. 'Really?' he queried
softly, his eyes gleaming with the crystalline brilliance of some dark, precious gem.

'I discovered that he wasn't what I wanted,' said
Eleni quietly, her eyes never leaving Constantine's
face. 'You see, I found that I'd been staring it in
the face all along.'

'I see.'

'Do you?' asked Eleni huskily.

Jade felt as though she were in the midst of a
nightmare, Eleni couldn't have made her feelings
for Constantine more obvious if she'd had a great
banner proclaiming her love erected and suspended
from wall to wall. And surely the dark rage which
simmered in the depths of Constantine's ebony eyes
was due to the fact that Eleni was now free, but it
had come too late for him. He had tied himself to
a loveless marriage to Jade. What price honour
now? For who in their right mind could possibly
fail to love a woman as glitteringly sophisticated
and beautiful as Eleni?

But wasn't she forgetting something? He *hadn't*
tied himself to her, had he? Not really. The marriage was always intended to be brief. Would he
now, as she suspected, abandon this so-called
'honeymoon' completely? With a hand that she

willed not to shake, Jade put her half-full coffee-cup on the small table beside her.

Constantine's eyes searched her face, his expression obdurate as they registered the draining of colour from her cheeks. He put his own cup down.

'Now,' he said smoothly, 'if you will excuse us, we will go to our room and freshen up. Jade is, I think, very tired.'

'But naturally,' murmured Eleni, her gaze taking in Jade's simple little lemon cotton sundress. 'And you will of course wish to change into something more suitable for this evening.'

'Of course,' agreed Jade evenly.

'Dinner will be at eight.' Eleni's smile showed tiny white teeth.

Like a ferret, thought Jade as she followed Constantine out of the room in silence, summoning up every bit of effort to smile politely at Eleni and her mother, because the last thing in the world she wanted was to let either of them know how much Eleni's unsubtle and predatory attitude towards Constantine had hurt her.

He led her along a cool, dim corridor and opened a dark wooden door to reveal a simply decorated room dominated by a vast double bed over which was slung a blindingly white bedspread. Large patterned cushions of white and blue added touches of colour, as did the blue paintwork around the shuttered windows. Their two suitcases were standing side by side on the floor, mocking her with their vision of unity. She supposed that Sophie had brought them in from the car while they had been sitting in the salon, drinking coffee.

Jade stared at the bed, her heart hammering as she tried and failed to block the mental pictures which swam up to torment her. Had there been some form of relationship between Constantine and Eleni in the past? Was that why she had stared at him with that hungry, almost wild look of longing? After all, stepbrother and sister were allowed to have a relationship by law, weren't they? Had his so-called *desire* for her now been deadened by the sight of his beautiful stepsister, freed from her engagement and obviously eager to find herself in Constantine's arms?

She fought the sick feeling in her stomach which threatened to swamp her, and stared up at Constantine, into the impenitent expression which had hardened the harsh features. It was over, she thought with immense sadness. It had never really begun.

He had moved towards her, and she knew that she had to put him straight before he touched her, because she couldn't trust herself to do the right thing if he touched her.

She backed away from him. 'I'm not sleeping with you here,' she told him quietly, and his eyes narrowed instantly into glittering black shards as she heard him draw in a deep breath.

'Oh, yes, you are,' he contradicted ruthlessly.

Her mouth dried. 'You can't *force* me...' she whispered.

'*Force* you?' He gave a cruel kind of smile. 'You little hypocrite! We both know that I wouldn't have to force you—erotic persuasion can be so much more effective, don't you think? But do not worry, Jade—I have no inclination to put it to the test. You can have the bed. I shall sleep in the chair——' His dark head indicated the roomy-looking but none the less unforgiving wicker chair which stood on the other side of the large room.

Her heart plummeted as she took in what he'd said. 'I have no inclination to put it to the test.' So he didn't even want her any more—the sight of Eleni had killed his desire stone-dead. But even knowing that, she was aware too that she wouldn't get a wink of sleep if he stayed in there with her. She would be longing for his possession, fighting every instinct she possessed to throw back the sheet and give him entry to her bed and body.

'Is that really necessary?' she demanded. 'There must be other bedrooms.' Including Eleni's, she thought with sick dismay.

His mouth tightened. 'Indeed there are. But I do not intend our marital spats to become public knowledge—not yet, in any case. There will be time enough for that. Marina and Eleni leave tomorrow morning. We can leave any decisions until then.'

So that was that, she thought, with a dull, empty ache in her heart. It was over. Eleni was his for the taking, and he wanted her now. And tomorrow he would release Jade from this farce of a marriage in order to pursue her.

Had that been the purpose behind his bizarre proposal in the first place? she wondered suddenly. Had she served her purpose by being brought here as his wife? Because perhaps Eleni was one of those women who were motivated by possessiveness— perhaps she hadn't realised how much she had wanted Constantine for herself, until she'd thought that someone else had him.

He glanced at his watch. 'You have only two hours before we are due to dine. I am sure that you could fill them most productively.' His eyes mocked her startled expression. 'Oh, don't worry, *agape mou*—you won't have to fend off my advances. I'm going for a walk. Be ready by eight.'

'I'm not very hungry.'

'I don't care. Just be there.'

'You can't make me!' she challenged.

'No?' he said softly, and she quickly turned away, rage and desire filling her veins with a pounding fire.

The *bastard*! The cold-hearted, cynical bastard! Even knowing that it was over, he still couldn't resist any opportunity to demonstrate his power over her.

She turned her back on him. 'I'd like to use the shower now,' she said coldly.

His response was equally cold. 'But of course.' And he slammed his way out of the room.

The bathroom was adjoined to their room, and Jade was surprised to see the luxuriously appointed fittings, not expecting such mod-cons in a place which was, to all intents and purposes, in the middle of nowhere.

She showered and changed into a short vampy dress of black satin, against which the pale fall of her hair stood out in startling contrast. If she was going out, she had decided in the shower, she was going to do it in style! She was just applying some blood-coloured lipstick in front of the mirror when Constantine returned. His face was set, and looked, she thought as she caught his reflection in the mirror, infinitely weary. She wondered whether he had in fact been out walking, or whether he had gone to Eleni, to seek solace in her arms, to make plans with her for their future.

He raised his eyebrows as he took in the amount of thigh she was showing, but gave her no greeting other than a short nod, then walked straight through to the bathroom.

She heard the sound of the shower running, and the hand which was applying mascara to her eye-lashes began to tremble as her mind began reluctantly to conjure up images of Constantine naked; his statuesque and magnificent golden body standing under the streaming jets of water. An image which stubbornly refused to disappear, and just the thought of it played absolute havoc with her already tightly stretched nerves.

But that was nothing to the effect he had on her when he walked back in the room, gleaming drop-lets of water still clinging to the dark olive of his skin and the dark hair which shadowed it. He was wearing nothing but the skimpiest of white towels slung low on his narrow hips.

Sweat broke out in beads on Jade's forehead, but she doggedly continued to apply her mascara, splodging on far more than she'd intended, and wondering whether his mocking smile meant that he'd noticed.

Dinner was the longest meal she'd ever had to endure, and anything less like a celebration she couldn't have imagined. The food was excellent, and so were the wines, and the table set out on the scented terrace under the light of the moon and the candles was simply breathtaking. But Eleni was clearly in a sniping mood, and Constantine obviously on edge.

Marina retired early, immediately after the coffee had been served, but Eleni looked set for the night, and after two cups of coffee Jade rose wearily to her feet.

'I'm going to turn in now,' she said. 'Please excuse me.'

Eleni nodded, then turned to Constantine. 'Stay and have a brandy with me,' she urged him. 'It's been too long since I've seen you.'

Jade's whole world hung on his answer, then came crashing around her ears as he nodded his dark head.

'Very well,' he concurred. 'Just the one, but first I must take my wife to her room.'

Feeling sick at heart, Jade stared at him in horror, wondering what kind of a hypocrite *he* must be if he could actually use the word 'wife' so inappropriately. She shook her head, so that her long hair swayed in a pale cloud around her head, the

long diamanté earrings she wore flashing starry light
around her neck. 'It doesn't matter, Constantine.
I know the way. Please don't bother.'

His mouth twisted. 'Very well.'

'Goodnight, Jade,' said Eleni, and Jade couldn't
miss the brief note of triumph which hovered in her
voice. 'It has been a delight to meet you.'

'Likewise,' said Jade evenly, then, before she gave
it all away, she turned quickly on her heel and away
to her room.

She had thought that sleep would elude her, that
she would stay awake all night in an agonised state,
listening for the sounds of betrayal—the muffled
giggles in the corridor, the deadened footsteps,
even, she thought in horror—the creaking of the
bed in another room. But perhaps she was wearier
than she'd thought—perhaps in times like this
nature could be almost kind and help her blot it all
out until tomorrow, or perhaps she'd done so much
thinking that her head simply couldn't take any
more. Because, whatever the reason, she found
herself drifting into the warm and numbing embrace of sleep, and when she opened her eyes again
she blinked at the ceiling in bewilderment, at the
patterns of sunlight which danced there, for a
moment not remembering where she was.

And then it all came back, and she turned her
head, expecting to find the room empty, but there
sat Constantine in the wicker chair, his black eyes
resting thoughtfully on her. He was, she registered
dully, still in the suit he'd worn down to dinner last
night. His face was etched with lines as though he

hadn't slept, and that, together with the crumpled
suit, seemed to bring her to her senses and she sat
up in bed, her blonde hair tumbling in wild disarray all over the thin straps of her ice-pink
camisole. She saw his eyes darken, and protectively
reached out for the matching wrap and pulled it
on.

'Jade——' he began, and she raised her hand to
halt him, because she knew that she could not bear
to hear him say it. She wasn't going to break down
in front of him. Let him have Eleni if he wanted,
but let him not say it.

'I want to go home,' she told him, and saw the
corners of his eyes crease in bewilderment.

'Home?' he echoed.

'Yes. Home. I'll get dressed, and then I'd like to
leave as soon as possible. Please say goodbye to
Eleni and her mother for me. And Sophie. I'd
prefer not to see anyone, if you don't mind.'

'They've gone,' he said flatly.

Now it was her turn to echo. 'Gone?'

He shifted his position in the chair and loosened
his tie. 'Yes, gone. Leaving us alone. At last. Because it's high time that you and I had a talk.'

'I don't think so.'

'You don't? Well, I do.'

And then she realised what had probably happened. Eleni had gone because it would be more
diplomatic if Constantine terminated the marriage
without his lover around. Perhaps there *was* that
touch of kindness in him which Stavros claimed he
had. Either that, or pity, or simply a dread of any

scenes which might ensue. But Jade had her dignity;
and she didn't want his kindness *or* his pity.

'It's all right, Constantine,' she said quietly,
marvelling that her voice should hold no giveaway
tremor. 'I know perfectly well what you want to
say to me.'

His eyebrows rose to become lost in the blackness
of his hair. 'You do?'

'Sure,' she said flippantly. 'You've made a
mistake. You thought you wanted me and for a
while you probably did. But now that Eleni is free—
well, I want you to know that I understand. I'm
releasing you from our marriage.'

A pulse began to beat insistently in the hollow
beneath one cheekbone. 'Just what the hell are you
talking about?' he demanded, from between gritted
teeth.

'You know darned well what I'm talking about!
You want *her*, not me—and she wants you. She
wants you so badly, you can feel it in the air. You
don't have to pretend any more. You spent the night
with her, OK, I understand, but now I just want
to get out of here, and as far away from you as
possible.'

'I spent the *night*,' he repeated ominously. 'With
Eleni?'

She'd had enough, flimsy nightdress or not, she
jumped out of the bed and ran for the bathroom.
'You know you did!' she sobbed, and wrenched the
door open, but he had waylaid her, pulling her violently into his arms, and she recoiled from the fury
on his face, the contempt she read in his eyes.

'You think I'm that kind of man?' he thundered. 'That I could make love to a woman while my wife lay in the next room?'

'But I'm *not* your wife, am I?' she shouted back. Wives were loved, cherished. 'Not really! Not properly!'

'Then why don't you start being my wife?' he ground out, and he pushed her down on to the bed.

'No!' she screamed out, as she felt the sinewy weight of him on top of her, so hard against the softness of her body, and her hands reached out to grip convulsively at his shoulders, supposedly, she thought, to push him away, but suddenly she wasn't doing any pushing. 'No,' she pleaded on a broken whisper. 'Not like this.'

'How then?' And his lips brushed softly against hers. 'Like this?'

For answer she gave a great sob in his arms, and then he cradled her to his chest, murmuring words in Greek which she did not understand, but which soothed and calmed her. When she'd stopped, he opened each eyelid with a gentle finger.

'Do you really think I wanted Eleni here?' he quizzed.

'You asked her to stay for as long as she liked!'

'Because she is my stepsister, and because we Greeks show respect and hospitality to our family. I don't love Eleni,' he said.

'But she loves you.'

He sighed. 'Yes,' he admitted. 'Or rather she thinks she does. She is a spoilt child who wants to take everything she sees—she always has been. She imagines that no man can resist her if she puts her mind to it. And last night, after dinner, I was not, as you imagined, making love to Eleni—instead I was telling her that I intended settling down to a happy and, I hope, a very long life, with you, my wife—if you can bring yourself to forgive me.'

Tears shimmered in her eyes at his cruelty. 'Don't lie!' she husked. 'Don't tell me any of your lies!'

He shook his head. 'I'm not lying. I speak from the heart—and I love you, Jade.'

The time for pussyfooting, she decided, was long past. 'You don't love me! You don't even trust me! You think that I'm a heartless journalist who'd do anything for a scoop—even selling her own secrets. You think that I'm a seasoned seductress who pretended to be a virgin——'

'I think none of those things,' he said quietly. 'I think that I have been an arrogant and blind fool and nearly lost what is most dear in all the world to me.'

'No, you don't,' she sniffed.

'Listen to me,' he said. 'You knew that I fell in love with you when we first met?'

'So you said.'

'*Don't* you?'

Jade moved restlessly, refusing to make it easier for him, aware as she did so, that he still held her closely.

His eyes glittered with some satanic fire as he spoke the soft, husky words. 'For years women had told me I was cold, arrogant, unfeeling; and maybe I was. And in my heart of hearts I suspected that

I was one of those men who never *can* fall in love. Perhaps the death of my mother made me equate love with loss. But even knowing that, logically, changed nothing. I did not seem able to feel emotion for a woman other than liking, and, occasionally—desire. But then I saw you, and it was like...' He shrugged, a rueful smile temporarily smoothing out the lines on his face. 'How can I explain what it was like? I don't think the words exist in either of our languages which could adequately describe it.

'An explosion, if you like. Or implosion. I was dizzy with it. Crazy. It was something to which no logic could be applied—overpowering—this need to be with you. I saw you and I fell in love with you. And then, when I met you—you were everything I dreamed you would be, only more. Intelligent, questioning, funny, sexy.' He gave a deep sigh. 'When you left the island I went half mad with wanting you. And that frightened me. For the first time in my life I felt no longer *in control*, and I found the experience disturbing. Profoundly disturbing. When I went back to work I found that I was restless, deferring decisions because I could not think straight and the only thing which occupied my thoughts, was you. Always you. I couldn't get you out of my mind.

'So I *forced* the rational side of my nature to try and analyse things—I told myself that I knew nothing about you. That it had all happened so quickly, on a magically beautiful island, that when faced with the stresses of everyday life the relationship would probably die a natural death. That I had kept my true identity secret, and that perhaps you would not care to be the wife of a very rich man—you who seemed content with the simple life we lived those few days.

'And then, when I found out who you were and what you did for a living, after my initial rush of anger I was almost *glad* to learn what I'd discovered about you.'

'*Glad*?' Jade echoed, totally confused.

'Yes, glad. Believing you to have lied to me and betrayed me, meant that I now no longer had any reason to love you, and consequently I felt back in control.'

'So you seduced me ruthlessly,' she accused him bitterly, trying to wriggle out from beneath him, but his hips made her firmly their prey and she was made achingly aware of the fact that he was turned on.

'Yes, I seduced you,' he agreed grimly. 'Which is not something I should be proud of, and yet it proved to be my undoing. Even believing myself to be hating you, I fell completely under your spell again. I'd never experienced lovemaking like that in my life—it blew my head off. I tried to convince myself that it was just a physical ache, that I could exorcise my desire for you by making love to you over and over and over again.' The corners of his mouth turned down in self-deprecating mockery. 'But I was trapped, enmeshed by you. The more I was with you, the more I grew to like you. As well as love you. My little virgin,' he added gently.

Jade's head was spinning. She wanted to believe him, oh, how she wanted to believe him. 'You told me I was no virgin. You said——' Her cheeks became stained scarlet as she remembered his cruel gibes, but she forced herself to repeat them. 'You said that if I was pretending to be a virgin, then I shouldn't...' But she couldn't finish the sentence.

His face became grave, and his voice was filled with anger, that even she could tell was directed inwards. 'Because, my darling, my feelings were in complete turmoil; that's why I lashed out at you the way I did. I felt honoured, humbled to be the man to whom you should offer the great gift of your virginity. And yet I was sick with remorse at the manner in which I took that gift. I should have wooed you quite gently in our marital bed, not taken you like that—so swiftly and so savagely. And then——' He hesitated. 'I was wary, too.'

'Wary?'

He gave a self-deprecating smile. 'Indeed, since I recognised that my days as a single man were numbered. Because you see, I had discovered during that quite blissful interlude on the sofa that it was not going to be easy to give you up; indeed, I suspected that it was going to be damn nigh impossible.'

He reached his hand out to stroke one finger gently down her cheek.

She let him.

'So you bought up the newspaper?' she quizzed. 'A bit over the top, wouldn't you say, Constantine?'

He didn't look in the least bit abashed. 'The situation called for dramatic measures.'

'Like forcing me to marry you by bribery?'

He shrugged. 'What else could I do? When you walked into your boss's office and gave me such a look of withering contempt, I knew that you would never agree to see me willingly again. I had to have you, and I was prepared to go to any lengths to do so.' He stared down at her, the ebony eyes boring bright fire into her soul.

'But you were so distant towards me, the morning after you made love to me at the Granchester.'

He gave a small sound of disapproval. 'Because I was furious with myself. I had seduced you that first time, almost brutally——'

'Not really brutally,' she corrected, being perfectly honest, because even if the intentions had been brutal the act itself had been bliss.

'Single-mindedly, then. I used my experience quite ruthlessly to get you to capitulate. After that I wanted to show you how sweet seduction could be, but I wanted to do that *after* we were married, to make amends for my behaviour, if you like. That night, when you turned to me, I felt so close to you, and I wanted to show you that closeness didn't necessarily have to culminate in making love. But you persuaded me to stay. And once again, I demonstrated that around you, all my self-control amounted to nothing.'

Jade gave him a look of satisfaction.

'Yes,' he teased her. 'You can afford to look smug!'

'Why didn't you tell me all this in London?'

'Because our time in London had been tainted with nothing but bad experience and misunderstanding. I was afraid that you were going to call my bluff and leave me, in London. That is why I wanted to start again, on the island. Alone. I brought you back to the island, where we had once been so happy—to rediscover our love for one another without the pressures which surrounded us in London. It was to be a honeymoon of the most traditional kind. The last thing in the world I imagined was to find my stepmother and sister waiting here, with my stepsister attempting, and managing, to drive a further wedge between us.' He paused. 'I need to know, *agape mou*, whether you can find it in your heart to forgive me, and whether there is any of the love left which you once felt for me?'

She suspected that her beautiful, arrogant Constantine already knew the answer to this question. His mouth was now inches away, but, much as she longed for him to kiss her, there were a few more things which *she* needed to get off her chest. '*You*, Constantine Sioulas,' she said firmly, 'are the most arrogant man I've ever met in my life.'

'I agree,' he said gravely.

'You think you can just barge your way through life, riding roughshod over people's feelings, doing exactly what *you* want, in order to get your own way. Don't you?'

'I do.' His lids hooded the spark in his eyes. 'And?'

'And I love you in spite of it, or because of it; I have done since the moment I set eyes on you, and it's never going to change, even though I probably shouldn't be telling you that.' But the softness in her eyes belied her words and she knew that, arrogant or not—she would never hide her love from him. Because Constantine was strong, yes—but at a cost. The cost of his lost years of childhood, unloved after his mother had died, a situation not unlike her own.

'Say it again,' he urged her softly, her powerful, beautiful man, and she needed no second bidding.

'I love you.'

He gave her a slow, slow smile. 'I don't think I could ever grow tired of hearing you say that.'

She vowed to tell him so every day of their lives, and the reality of their future suddenly hit Jade like a gloriously starry blow to the heart. 'Oh, Constantine,' she began, but the sentence was never completed because he started kissing her.

Some time later he raised his dark head and looked down at her.

'My main residence is in New York. Do you mind?'

'Mind?' She gave him a dazed, dreamy smile. 'I know that this is the most corny thing to say, but I'd live anywhere with you, Constantine.'

He wound a strand of bright gold hair round and round his finger. 'At the moment I travel all over the world, and I want you to travel with me, but when the babies come—well, then we won't be so nomadic.'

Babies! Jade wriggled her toes with anticipation, then kissed every inch of his face. 'Just so long as we can have our holidays here,' she murmured.

'I promise. But only if you promise me that you'll write that book you once told me you thought you had in you.'

She kissed the end of his nose, her eyes sparkling with mischief. 'Funny you should say that—I happen to have the first twenty pages in my suitcase.'

'Then I am afraid I shall have to confiscate it,' he said gravely. 'This is, after all, our honeymoon—and I intend to spend the whole time making love to you.'

'Oh, Constantine,' she said breathily, helpless with a love for him which overwhelmed her, her feelings shining from her eyes, so that he grinned—that rare and bright and irresistible grin.

'Jade,' he whispered, and buried his head in her shoulder, and when he raised it again he looked like a man at peace with himself, but a man with something else on his mind too.

'And now,' he murmured, '*sweet* bride, what shall we do next? Any ideas?'

Her heart swelled with love, and her body tingled with the glorious anticipation of his touch. 'Oh, *yes*, my darling,' she whispered, and reached up to kiss him. 'More than you'd ever believe.'

MILLS & BOON

are proud to present...

A set of warm, involving romances in which you can meet some fascinating members of our heroes' and heroines' families. Published each month in the Romance series.

Look out for "Simply the Best" by Catherine Spencer in July 1995.

Family Ties: Romances that take the family to heart.

MILLS & BOON

KIDS & KISSES

Kids & Kisses—where kids and romance go hand in hand.

This summer Mills & Boon brings you Kids & Kisses— a set of titles featuring lovable kids as the stars of the show!

Look out for
Love Without Measure by Caroline Anderson
in July 1995 (Love on Call series).

Kids…one of life's joys, one of life's treasures.

Kisses…of warmth, kisses of passion, kisses from mothers and kisses from lovers.

In Kids & Kisses…every story has it all.

SPRING FLOWER COMPETITION

How would you like a years supply of Temptation books ABSOLUTELY FREE? Well, you can win them all! All you have to do is complete the word puzzle below and send it in to us by 31st December 1995. The first 5 correct entries picked out of the bag after that date will win a years supply of Temptation books (*four books every month - worth over £90*). What could be easier?

COWSLIP									
	L	L	E	B	E	U	L	B	Q
BLUEBELL	P	R	I	M	R	O	S	E	A
PRIMROSE	I	D	O	D	Y	U	I	P	R
DAFFODIL	L	O	X	G	O	R	S	E	Y
ANEMONE	S	T	H	R	I	F	T	M	S
DAISY	W	P	I	L	U	T	F	K	I
GORSE	O	E	N	O	M	E	N	A	A
TULIP	C	H	O	N	E	S	T	Y	D
HONESTY									
THRIFT									

PLEASE TURN OVER
FOR DETAILS OF HOW
TO ENTER

HOW TO ENTER

Hidden in the grid are various British flowers that bloom in the Spring. You'll find the list next to the word puzzle overleaf and they can be read backwards, forwards, up, down, or diagonally. When you find a word, circle it or put a line through it.

After you have completed your word search, don't forget to fill in your name and address in the space provided and pop this page in an envelope (you don't need a stamp) and post it today. Hurry - competition ends 31st December 1995.

Mills & Boon Spring Flower Competition,
FREEPOST,
P.O. Box 344,
Croydon,
Surrey. CR9 9EL

Are you a Reader Service Subscriber?   Yes ❏   No ❏

Ms/Mrs/Miss/Mr _____

Address _____

_____

_____ Postcode _____

One application per household.   F

You may be mailed with other offers from other reputable companies as a result of this application. If you would prefer not to receive such offers, please tick box. ❏

COMP395